GONE
TOO
SOON

GONE TOO SOON

MELODY CARLSON

WhiteSpark

GONE TOO SOON

WhiteSpark Publishing
a division of WhiteFire Publishing

13607 Bedford Rd NE
Cumberland, MD 21502

www.WhiteSpark-Publishing.com

ISBN: 978-1-946531-10-0 (paperback)
     978-1-946531-11-7 (digital)
     978-1-946531-49-0 (hardback)

One

I KNOW IT'S WRONG TO STEAL—EVEN WORSE to steal your sister's diary. But I just can't seem to stop myself. As I tiptoe down the hallway from my bedroom to Hannah's, I can hear Mom thumping around downstairs in the kitchen. It sounds like she's in a mood too, throwing pots and pans around. But no one else is home—providing the perfect opportunity to grab Hannah's diary and make a clean getaway.

I've been planning this crime ever since I discovered my older sister's secret hiding place when I snuck into her room a couple days ago. I trespassed forbidden territory to "borrow" a swimsuit for the last day of school swim party—but I was surprised to uncover Hannah's diary in the process. So all day yesterday, I obsessed over that small blue book. Like it was calling my name. And since this is the first day of summer vacation with nothing but

boredom in sight, I'm compelled to pull off this despica-
ble act. I plan to secretly read my dead sister's diary—
from cover to cover.

A fresh wave of guilt washes over me as I enter Hannah's silent room. As always, this space, like my sister, is
picture-perfect. It's like a spread from one of the "shabby
chic" magazines Hannah used to study almost as much as
her well-worn Bible. Such a contrast to the hodgepodge
rat's nest in my room. Not only does everything in here
stay clean—thanks to my mom's obsession with preserv-
ing everything "as is"—the style seems to improve with
age. From the pastel patchwork quilt and pillows on her
neatly made bed to the rustic bookshelf and desk that she
painted herself, it's all perfection… just like Hannah.

I jump when I hear a loud clang downstairs—a reminder that Mom would throw a horrific hissy fit if she found
me in Hannah's room. And yet my feet remain glued to
the hardwood floor as I stare around the room—all which
silently screams a security warning: *Hannah-Hannah-Han-
nah! A thief has entered your room!*

Get in and get out, I remind myself as I creep across the
pastel rag rug that Grandma Josephson helped Hannah to
crochet several years ago. Probably the beginning of my
sister's shabby chic obsession. I go directly to her bureau,
sliding out the bottom drawer where her athletic wear
is all neatly folded, shorts and tanks and sweats… with
swimsuits on the right. Right where I spotted it before, her
diary is tucked at the bottom of the drawer, wrapped in her

old middle-school swim-team suit. With pounding heart, I grab up the diary and, sliding it under my loose t-shirt, I secure it in the top of my cutoffs... just in case Mom's on the prowl. Then I carefully straighten the drawer so that it looks exactly as before—well, except for a missing bikini that's probably still a soggy wad in my backpack.

Glancing over my shoulder to be sure Mom's not lurking in the doorway and ready to bust me, I make my swift getaway. Feeling like a felon, I slip down the hallway and back into my room, quietly closing the door before I slide my black beanbag chair in front of it. Not that the beanbag could keep anyone out, but it makes me feel more secure as I pull out the diary, running a hand over the pebbly leatherette cover.

I still remember how jealous I felt when Grandma Josephson gave Hannah this diary for her sixteenth birthday—almost two years ago now. Never mind that I've always known Hannah was her favorite—everyone's favorite—I really thought the retro diary with its brass lock, tiny key, and faux leather cover was pretty cool. Very funky old school. And since I'm the one who excels in writing, it seemed more fitting to give it to me than Hannah. Not that anyone in my family would agree.

"This was presented to me by my grandmother when I turned sixteen," Grandma explained to Hannah. "I suppose it's almost an antique now. But I never wrote in it. Not a single word." She smiled wistfully. "Later on in life... when it was too late... I wished that I had." She went on to explain how teen years were very special and pass very quickly, and how Hannah should keep a record of them. And based on the various times I caught my older sister frantically scribbling away in this book, I know that she had.

I don't have the key, but quickly discover the flimsy brass lock is easy to pick with a large safety pin. Though as I flop down on my beanbag chair, I vaguely wonder where Hannah hid the key. Not that I need it now. Do I feel guilty as I open my dead sister's private journal? Of course! But does that stop me? No way! I'm like an addict who needs a fix—it might be wrong, but I gotta have it!

I'm caught off guard to see that the first entry isn't until New Year's Day—almost six months after Hannah received it. Of course, it's not last January. Hannah was dead by then. But it appears she never opened this diary when Grandma Josephson gave it to her that summer. That surprises me. I figured my Type A sister would've faithfully written in it every single day since her sixteenth birthday. It seems I was wrong.

January 1,
Dear Diary,

I assume that's how one starts an entry in a diary, but I must admit it feels a little weird. And I doubt that I'll continue to address this funny little book like that. But I also doubt that I'll continue to write in here. Not because I don't enjoy the process of writing. But only because I have so little to write about. My life is basically boring. I am basically boring. My friends are basically boring. It seems like we all just do the same thing over and over again. Nothing ever changes. And the truth is—I don't like it. I'm well aware that everyone around me assumes I'm always upbeat and congenial. Naturally, I play along. I'm always called cheerful and positive. Along with a few other labels I don't like. Like Polly-Hannah—AKA Pollyanna. Ugh!

A sharp jab of guilt interrupts me. Not the shame for reading my dead sister's diary. That's bad enough, but I remember that I'm the one who first labeled her *Polly-Hannah*. I always used a snarky tone when I called her that. Even in front of her friends, who later teased her with the name too. Probably, if I'm being honest, I taunted her as much out of envy as irritation. I didn't understand how anyone could be so obnoxiously optimistic all the time. But that was Hannah. My perfect sister. Taking a deep breath, I continue to read.

I hate that I have to keep up this sweetly smiling image for everyone—acting like everything is so great in my world—when the truth is I pretty much hate my life. Wow, I can't believe I just wrote those words. But it's true! I HATE MY LIFE! What a relief to put it on paper. Maybe confession really is good for the soul. Would I want anyone to read these words? Never! So maybe that's the beauty of a diary. A girl can just say it like it is without worrying that someone is going to totally freak out. A reminder that I better find a very secure place to hide this book. Not that I expect anyone to read it.

Hopefully no one in my family is a snoop! Because I know Mom and Dad would be seriously shocked to know how I really feel about certain things. Like that I hate my life. They always assume that I'm perfectly fine—and I know it makes them feel good…and proud. If Mom discovered the truth she'd probably make an appointment with her therapist <u>for me</u>. Besides my parents, I really wouldn't want my baby sister Maddie to read this either—although I doubt she would since she is for the most part a very law-abiding and genuinely sweet ten-year-old. As for Kiera, well, I wouldn't put it past her. She might only be fourteen, but she is scarily sophisticated for her age. But if Kiera does read this—as angry as I would be at her—I suspect she might understand some of my conflicted feelings. Because Kiera has a dark side. A natural pessimism that she doesn't bother to keep hidden from anyone. Kiera might actually get me on some levels. Except that she's so mean she'd probably use my words against me. Knowing Kiera, she might

even resort to blackmail or extortion. Sure, she's
my sister, but I do not trust her.

Once again, I have to stop reading. It hurts to know
that this is how Hannah really felt about me. Although
most of what she wrote is absolutely true. And she was
right to distrust me—I guess I'm proving it right now.
What kind of person steals and reads her sister's diary?
Hannah was right. I really do have a dark side. And the
truth is—it scares me too. But not enough to stop me from
continuing to read. In fact, I'm even more interested now
than before. I doubt I will ever be able to stop. Not until
I read the entire book. And I can tell by flipping through
the nearly filled book, there are hundreds of entries. I
hungrily continue.

So my only defense is to keep my diary securely
locked and hidden. That is if I really plan to record
my deepest darkest secrets in here. Because I re-
alize that could be risky. But since I already feel
better after writing just one entry, I suspect that I
will keep up with it. So here's to a new year—the
reason I wanted to write in the first place was to
put down some resolutions. Although I honestly
don't expect my life to change or get better. But
maybe I really am an optimist.

So… here are my New Year's Resolutions:

1. *Stop being such a hypocrite and pretending every-thing is okay when it's not.*
2. *Find out who I really am and don't be afraid to be that person.*
3. *Get genuine friends who will accept the real me—not just Polly-Hannah.*
4. *Find out why I feel so unhappy underneath my usual smiley face and do something about it.*
5. *Keep writing <u>honestly</u> in my diary.*
6. *Break up with Wyatt. No matter what Haley says!*

Now this is a surprise since I assumed Wyatt was the one who broke up with Hannah last year. They'd been off-and-on since they were about fifteen. But Wyatt was always like *Mr. Perfect*. The kind of boyfriend that earned the parents' seal of approval. He was student council president, both athletic and academic, and involved in our church's youth group. But he and Hannah broke up in her junior year—probably not too long after she wrote that into her resolution list.

I'm about to turn the page when I hear my mom scream-ing at me to come downstairs to help her with something. I know better than to protest or to be too pokey. I don't need her storming into my room. My mother, when an-gry, has no respect for privacy. Plus Dad already warned me, before he went to play golf, that Mom was feeling particularly edgy today. Okay, I get that. But doesn't she realize that she's not the only one who gets uptight? Not that I'll point this reality out to her. I really don't need the drama right now.

As I shove the diary under my mattress, I yell that I'm coming. I'll need to find a more secure hiding place—soon. Then I rush downstairs to find my mother dressed for work and staring angrily at her phone.

"Empty the dishwasher," she commands without looking at me. "I've got potatoes on the stove. Take them off and drain them when the timer goes off. They're for potato salad and..." She looks at me with a frown. "I'd ask you to take over making the potato salad for me, except that I know you're not *into* cooking. Not like your..." As she stops herself and turns away, I consider finishing her sentence for her. *Not like your sister.* Fortunately, I have the good sense to keep my mouth shut as I open the dishwasher.

"And then you can clean the kitchen. And clear out the clutter in the great room. I suspect it's mostly your stuff anyway. Then give the powder room a swipe down and—"

"Is someone coming here or something?" I slide out a rack full of dishes.

"I already told you that Grandma Josephson is coming today. To pick up Maddie. *Remember?*" Her voice drips with irritation, her usual tone reserved for me.

"I thought Maddie was at Olivia's for the weekend—"

"Seriously?" Mom glares at me as if she'd like to whack me with the wooden spoon she's just picked up. Not that she would do that. It's not her style to physically harm anyone. But there are no holds barred with verbal abuse. "Don't you *ever* listen to me, Kiera?"

"I, uh, I try to but I—"

"You did know that Grandma Josephson was taking Maddie home with her for the entire summer, did you not?"

"Yeah, but I thought that was next week and—"

"Your grandmother changed her mind. She already had to drive halfway here to meet up with some friends this morning. So she'll be here this afternoon. She will have dinner with us, spend the night, and then take Maddie home with her tomorrow morning." Mom's eyes look kind of wild now, like she's about to totally lose it. "Is that too much for you to take in, Kiera?"

I have to swallow hard not to spew back what I'm really thinking. I want to scream, *I'm sorry I'm not your favorite daughter! I'm sorry I'm not perfect like Hannah. I'm sorry you're such a bi—*

"Are you even listening to me?" she demands.

"Yeah," I mumble, carefully setting a plate on the granite countertop.

"And you heard what I asked you to do?" she persists. "You were actually listening for a change?"

"Yeah," I answer in a robotic tone. "The dishwasher. The potatoes. The great room. The powder room. Grandma Josephson coming. I got it, Mom."

"I would do it all myself—like usual—but a client just

called about seeing a house. Unlike your dad, *I* have to work on weekends. So you'll just have to fend for yourself for a few hours."

I want to point out that I always fend for myself, but I know better. That would only throw fuel on the fire. Mom is obviously stressing, and quite frankly, I just can't handle a conflict. Instead, I continue to cautiously remove plates, one by one, just like she's told me to do it a hundred times before.

"Another thing, Kiera."

"What?" I turn to see she's got her eyes on her phone, but her mouth looks grim.

"Clean up that pigsty you call a bedroom. I swear I could smell it when I went down the hallway yesterday. I want it cleaned up before your grandmother gets here. Understand?"

Okay, now this just really ticks me off. *Really,* she can *smell* my room? I mean seriously, how much am I supposed to take from this woman? Does she really think I have no feelings?

"I mean it, Kiera. I don't want your grandmother to assume that I've raised a total slob and don't have—"

"What if you did?" I instantly regret this, but it's already out there.

Now she lowers her phone and comes closer, giving me a very intense examination, as if seeing me for the first time…and there is disgust in her eyes. "Okay, fine, then, Kiera. You asked for it, didn't you? So while we're at it, your room isn't the only problem here. *You* are a complete and total slob. An embarrassment to both your father and me. Probably Maddie too. Just look at that filthy t-shirt. I'll bet you've been wearing it for a week or more. And those cutoffs? Could they be any shorter? Or dirtier. And those nasty flip-flops look like they're diseased. One would think your parents refuse to buy you any clothes. And you know that's not true. I would gladly take you—"

"You know that I don't really care about clothes, Mom." I give her my best bored expression. "Materialism doesn't appeal to me."

"Oh, yeah, right. I forgot. You're into idealism. Our *bohemian* child. Our little artist in residence with a shabby sort of chic that's all her own." Her words drip with sarcasm. "Well, FYI, little girl. This luxurious residence happens to be owned by your materialistic parents. So while you're living under our roof, you'll comply to our—"

"Give it up, Mom!" The words burst out of me, flying around like shrapnel. "You can't remake me into Hannah! No matter how hard you try, it's not going to happen. So you might as well get over it. *Hannah is gone.* Okay? She is not coming back. And I cannot replace her!" And now the tears are about to come, but I'm determined not to break down in front of this woman. "I'm sorry!" I shout angrily as I march out of the kitchen. "I'm sorry my sister is dead! I'm sorry you blame me for it!"

Two

MOIRA JOSEPHSON HAD ALWAYS HATED losing her temper. And for decades she'd managed her emotions with relative ease. But as she stormed out to her car, she couldn't resist kicking the watering can that someone had carelessly left in the driveway. Better than punching someone. Like Kiera. Somehow she had to get control of this. She couldn't meet new clients with fire in her eyes. But regaining control seemed harder and harder. Especially when it came to her button-pushing teenage daughter. Was Kiera's singular goal to drive her stark-raving mad? How long would it take?

Moira dug through her oversized designer bag, frantically searching for car keys. She never used to have such difficulty tracking simple things like this. She used to be so organized. But her life was steadily unraveling.

She shook her purse, cursing quietly over the elusive key chain. "Come on," she told herself. "Take it easy…just breathe." She closed her eyes, digging deeper until, to her relief, she found the evasive keys.

Still breathing deeply, Moira started her car. She had always considered herself reserved and controlled and mature. She had great respect for etiquette and protocol. So much so that a few fellow realtors had even dubbed her the *Ice Queen*. Behind her back, of course. And, of course, she never showed that it bothered her. Not yet anyway. Her tires squealed as she backed out of the driveway—too fast. And then, knowing it was wrong, she kept the pedal to the metal as she roared down the quiet street. Yes, she was being juvenile, stupidly irresponsible…and it was embarrassing to imagine what her neighbors might be saying to each other. The problem was that she simply didn't care.

She slowed down as she got nearer to town. It wasn't unusual to see a traffic cop on a side street, and it would be humiliating to get pulled over. Her plan was to swing by the office, grab some home brochures, and get to the Lawrence house before the clients arrived. It wasn't a bad listing, but Linda Lawrence had four cats and seemed oblivious to the feline aroma. Hopefully, she'd taken Moira's directions seriously today. The cats were supposed to be secured in the garage and the floors and furnishings "de-furred." And Moira was armed with an aerosol can of natural orange spray that could conceal the most obnoxious odors but would unfortunately not poison the cats.

After she gathered some brochures in the right neighborhood and price range, Moira felt slightly calmer and, with time to spare, managed to drive to Warren Heights within the speed limit. She let herself into the house, doing a quick walk-through to make sure the house was at its best, turning on lights, plumping pillows, and liberally spraying orange spray in every room before she opened a couple of windows and turned on some overhead fans.

As she paced back and forth through the well-designed kitchen, waiting for her out-of-town clients to arrive, she replayed that last scene with Kiera—reexamining her own role. Why had Moira gotten so mad? Why did she always react so vehemently to Kiera's words? Why had she felt so completely enraged? She could never admit this to anyone, but it had taken all of her self-control not to strike out at Kiera. And this was ridiculous because Moira had never physically abused anyone. The thought of her hitting Kiera was so disgusting that she felt thoroughly ashamed. What was happening to her?

Of course, it had been a bit shocking to hear Kiera's claim that she was being blamed for Hannah's death. But wasn't it true? Moira grabbed a paper towel, vigorously polishing the chrome kitchen faucet. In all fairness, Hannah would still be alive if Kiera hadn't changed her mind that night. So it was obviously Kiera's choice and Kiera's fault that Hannah was dead. Kiera certainly couldn't blame anyone else for her own actions.

Moira continued moving around the kitchen, shining chrome knobs and handles in an attempt to make it all sparkle and glow. She had always believed that people should own up to their mistakes. It was simply a part of growing up. And Kiera was always claiming she was so grownup—why couldn't she own up to the part she played in her sister's death? Why was that so difficult for her?

It didn't help that Kiera refused to see the counselor anymore. It was as if she enjoyed being stuck. Moira felt that Kiera liked playing the role of the *dark daughter*. It was the perfect excuse to going around looking like a bag lady and sporting a nasty attitude about everyone and everything. And that hair! Moira didn't even want to go there, but every time she looked at the way Kiera had hacked off her thick brown hair, well, it made Moira want to scream.

But enough was enough. And it was high time that Kiera got over herself. This was the main reason that Moira had agreed with Alex's mother about taking Maddie away for the summer. It would allow Moira more freedom to deal openly with her stubborn middle child. And Kiera was begging to be dealt with!

It wasn't as if Moira didn't love Kiera. Of course, she did. It was simply that she could barely stand the girl. If only Kiera would show some remorse...or offer an apology…. If she could just make a little effort, well, it might be easier for everyone to move on.

The sound of the doorbell startled Moira back into the present. She tossed the paper towel, smoothed her blonde bobbed hair into place and, going into pleasant-faced realtor mode, strolled to the front door and, smiling warmly, welcomed the older couple inside. She'd only been selling real estate for a few years, but she knew she was good at this. She also knew that if things didn't start improving with Alex, she might need these commissions for more than just mad money. No one had used the D word yet, but she sometimes felt that divorce was inevitable.

Moira knew from this morning's conversation with Mrs. Mitchell that, because their daughter lived nearby, she and her husband wanted a house in Warren Heights. But as they went from room to room, it seemed that all they could do was find fault. Where there was carpet, they wanted hardwood. Where there was hardwood, they wanted tile.

"And this backyard is too big," Mr. Mitchell declared. "I don't want to spend all my spare time on yard work."

"All the lots in Warren Heights are the same size," Moira explained. "Most people consider them small lots."

"Maybe we need a bigger house," Mrs. Mitchell said absently. "That would make for less yard."

"I did bring some other listings," Moira said brightly. Although she'd prefer them to buy her listing, she wasn't opposed to showing them others. Half a commission was better than no commission. "There are about six others for sale in this subdivision. Several of them are bigger and—"

"But the plan was to downsize," Mr. Mitchell reminded his wife. "I wanted to keep it under 2,000 square feet—and in this price range."

Moira switched over to distraction mode, pointing out upgrades that the couple might've overlooked, hoping to draw them back in. "So many people are downsizing these days," she said to Mr. Mitchell. "And I think this home is the perfect size for a couple who are looking ahead to retirement. Not too big, not too small. And the yard might seem large, but it does afford you some good privacy. And lots of the homeowners here hire out their landscaping. That's what we do at my house. I'd happily refer some names if you'd like." But the more she talked, the more she knew she was losing them. At least on this particular house.

She pulled the brochures from her bag, holding them up. "I can make some quick phone calls and see if we can—"

"No, thank you." Mr. Mitchell held up a hand to stop her. "Didn't my wife tell you that we already have a realtor? He's ready to show us—"

"You have another real estate agent?" Moira tried to keep her tone even.

"Yes." He jerked his thumb toward his wife. "She called you directly since this was your listing and she was so eager to see it, but we have a guy ready to show us some other houses this afternoon. A friend of our daughter's. That's why we drove to town."

"I'm sorry." Mrs. Mitchell looked flustered. "I thought I mentioned that to you on the phone."

Moira felt certain she hadn't, but she knew better than to show her irritation. It wasn't in her best interest to burn bridges with anyone. And so she smiled and firmly shook their hands. "Well, I hope you find exactly what you're looking for. Warren Heights is a very desirable neighborhood and most listings here don't last for long. Anyway, if I can be of any future service to you, please, feel free to give me a call." She handed them both a business card, still smiling stiffly.

They thanked her and somewhat sheepishly made their exit. She wrote a quick note to Linda, explaining that the house probably wasn't a good fit for the clients and thanked her for containing the cats and removing the fur. Moira closed the windows and turned off the lights and fans and then, unable to control herself, swore loudly as she stomped toward the front door. But as she got into her car she was determined not to speed through this neighborhood. Still, it took all of her control not to.

Moira wished she had someone to talk to…a good solid friend who really knew how to listen. But, for the life of her, she could think of no one. In the past, she had often relied on Hannah in moments like this. Hannah had been an amazing listener, very caring and wise for her age. In some ways she and Hannah had been very similar. They looked so much alike that it wasn't unusual for a store clerk to ask if they were sisters. Oh, Moira knew it could be a sales tactic, but she'd enjoyed it just the same. How she missed those times. Hannah had enjoyed shopping as much as Moira. And she'd enjoyed going out to lunch with her mother too. In many ways, their relationship had been more like friends than mother-daughter. But as much alike as they were, they were different too. Hannah was much more outgoing. She could easily befriend anyone. Meanwhile, Moira held back. Well, unless she was with Hannah.

Moira hadn't really planned to drive to the cemetery today. But like so many other days when she wound up standing in front of her daughter's grave like this, it was as if she'd arrived on autopilot. Almost like the sleepwalker who wakes up standing in front of the refrigerator biting into a stick of butter.

"Why, oh, why?" she said between sobs. "Why, why, why, God? Why did you take her? What good does it do anyone? Why would a loving God do this to us?" These were exactly the same questions she always asked. Every time she came up here like this. And just like all the other times, no answers came to her today. God never parted the clouds, never spoke in a deep, wise voice, never consoled her… nothing.

For all she knew God was just sitting up there on his big fat throne, mocking her. Or worse yet, he wasn't there at all. Never had been. It was all just a big cosmic joke on anyone foolish enough to fall for it. And that meant Pastor Jim was wrong when he'd claimed that Hannah was up there singing and dancing in heaven, and that God had wanted their beautiful daughter simply to brighten his day. But if Pastor Jim was just as deceived as Moira felt right now, it meant that her daughter's life had been randomly snuffed out...for no good reason...and that Moira would never see her again. She broke into fresh sobs. How could she live with that?

Three

I WASN'T SURPRISED TO HEAR THE FRONT door slam when Mom left the house, followed by the sound of her Volvo roaring down the driveway. Never mind what the neighbors would think. No one in our house seems to care about that anymore. I followed her example by slamming my own door shut and, to relieve some of my stress, I shouted a string of profanities, punched my beanbag chair, and loudly declared my undying hatred for my mother.

Half an hour later, I'm still so angry that I almost wish my mother was dead. *Almost.* But I can't really go there. I'm not that ignorant…or selfish. Our messed-up family can only take so much. I know this. And, fine, I didn't expect my mother to come back and attempt to make amends with me. Or me with her. That's just how we roll these days. No more *I'm sorry* or *I forgive you* like we were brought up to say. We all let the "sun go down on our wrath" nowadays.

No one has verbalized as much, but our old Christian clichés and platitudes flew right out the window not long after Hannah died. Now it's all about blame and shame and guilt and grief…and this seething, deep-rooted hatred that taints everything. Such a lovely way for a nice church-going family to live.

Not that anyone besides Maddie goes to church anymore. And I've noticed she's been getting a little slack lately. Oh, we all made a good show at Hannah's memorial service in January, sitting up front in our packed-out church, "celebrating" her short, beautiful life and pretending we were so happy that Hannah was up there "dancing in heaven," like Pastor Jim described her. But as far as I'm concerned, God was buried with my sister that day. I'm done with religion.

And my parents don't know this yet, but I'm done with them too. I've been working on an emancipation strategy ever since I turned sixteen a couple months ago. Even though I'll only be a junior this fall, I plan to graduate a year early. And then I am so out of here. Even if I don't get accepted into a college or find a job, I'm leaving. I don't even care if I have to live in a cardboard box beneath the bridge. It would be better than *this*. If I got along with my grandparents, I would beg them to take me for the summer too. But their invitation was only for Maddie. And, although my little sister keeps her feelings to herself, I know she needs them right now.

Despite my self-centeredness that Mom is always pointing out, I do feel sorry for Maddie. She's always caught in the middle. She tries to see everyone's side, tries to be the peacemaker. A tough assignment for a twelve-year-old. Not to mention thankless…and hopeless. When her efforts fall by the wayside, she takes refuge in reading. I'm sure she's read about a hundred books since Hannah died. She even had her nose in her e-reader at the memorial service. I secretly suspect her reading obsession is why she had to get glasses last month. Between Maddie's braces, glasses, allergies, and eczema—which has gotten worse—I realize my little sister has some pretty big challenges ahead. And yet I'm still a bit jealous that she gets to escape our madhouse this summer.

At the same time, I'm glad she's getting away. Maddie needs to escape our war zone. She's not a natural fighter, and I've recently observed my mom going after her lately—which makes me go totally ballistic. And that can get ugly. But at least I can hold my own with Mom. And with Maddie out of the way, I won't need to control my "little outbursts." Plus, I can call Mom on hers. It won't be long before she welcomes my emancipation.

Yeah, it won't be pretty around here this summer, but it's not like I can avoid it. I've done a decent job of alienating most of my friends—refuges I might've sought out in BHD. Before Hannah Died. My only hope seems to be getting a job. Hopefully a full-time one. But I haven't heard back on any of the applications I turned in last weekend before school let out. I only applied for restaurant jobs and only at the nicest ones in town. Not that I think I'd make a particularly good waitress or like the idea of taking orders from cranky diners, but I've heard that tips make it worthwhile.

I check my phone just to be sure I haven't missed a text or call from one of them. I wish Leonardi's would call me with a waitress job, but no such luck. And, hearing the timer going off in the kitchen, I remember the potatoes... as well as the list of chores Mom threw at me before her tantrum. But before I leave my room, I remember Hannah's diary under my mattress. Pretty obvious hiding place. So I shove it into my grimy backpack which I toss into my closet, covering it with dirty clothes. Probably what my mother thinks is smelling a bit ripe. Not that I give a rip.

As I go downstairs, I remember the counselor I visited a few times, and how she always began by listing the Stages of Grief to me. Like I cared. Counselor Claudia was convinced that I was stuck in the depression stage. Well, duh. Who isn't depressed after her sister tragically dies? Tell me something I *don't* know. Of course, Claudia then felt the need to list the symptoms of depression to me. I swear that woman has a fixation on listing lists—maybe she has OCD. Naturally, Claudia got stuck on my obvious *disinterest in my appearance.* Like wearing dirty jeans was the worst thing a girl could do. I suspect it was because my mother had complained about my lack of personal hygiene to her. Anyway, that was the last time I went to see Counselor Claudia.

I turn off the oven timer and the burner, hoping that scorched smell doesn't mean the potatoes are ruined. So maybe I'm not really cut out for restaurant work after all. I pour cold water over the potatoes like Mom said to then leave the pan in the sink and return to unloading the dishwasher. To me this is the drudgery of drudgery.

I still find it difficult to accept that Hannah *liked* helping in the kitchen. I used to think she was just faking it to get on mom's good side...back when Mom had a good side. Although that was irrelevant when it came to Hannah. I swear I never saw my mom ever say a cross word to my older sister. Everyone knew that Hannah was mom's favorite. No one in our family would dispute this. Hannah didn't need to jump through any hoops to win points with Mom. They were handed to her on a silver platter.

As I clatter around the kitchen, I remember how Hannah was totally comfortable in here. Sometimes she'd come down here in the evening and just whip up some cookies or brownies. Sometimes she'd make a cake— for no real reason. And although she used boxed mixes, she wasn't afraid to crack open a cookbook. I honestly don't get that, but the truth is I secretly admired it. And I miss her peanut-butter cookies.

Thinking about her like this does not help me. Not one

bit. Especially after reading her diary. The old familiar lump is growing in my throat again. I can feel tears building up inside of me.

Instead of giving in to unwanted grief, I slip my earbuds into place and crank up my music. Playing it so loudly that my ears will be ringing but my feelings are subdued. I continue to straighten the house, getting it ready for my grandmother's visit like I think she'll be giving it the white glove test. Okay, I know my cleaning standards aren't that good. Never good enough for my mom anyway, although I doubt she'll mention it—not while Grandma Josephson is here. After that, well, I don't really care. Finally, I'm done...sort of. And, not to appease my mother, but more to avoid my grandmother's general disapproval, I take a quick shower and change into a slightly cleaner and more presentable outfit. I'll have the rest of summer to drive my mother insane with my grunge look.

As I towel my short hair, I marvel at how quickly it dries nowadays. Sure, it looks like someone hacked it off with a chainsaw. And the truth is I sometimes regret what I did that night. But I think it was an honest-to-goodness case of temporary insanity. It's a good thing that no one got seriously hurt. It started when I woke up in the middle of the night just pulling on my hair—I mean really pulling like I wanted to rip it out by the roots. And since I used to be a cutter and know a thing or two about self-inflicted pain and mutilation, I decided I should nip this neurosis in the bud. So I ran down to the kitchen and, unable to locate the scissors, I took a really sharp knife and began hacking away on my long brown hair.

I don't really remember what happened after that or even going back to bed—but I do remember waking to my mother's screams. I thought for sure she was being murdered, but when I found her downstairs, she was just staring in horror at the brown hair all over the kitchen floor. Naturally, I cleaned it up. But when my family asked me why I did what I did, all I could say was, "I don't know." And honestly, I don't know. I think even Claudia the Counselor was stumped by it.

I'm just tossing my towel into the hamper when I hear the doorbell ringing downstairs. Irritated that Maddie's not back from Olivia's to deal with this, I hurry down to let Grandma Josephson in the house. I try to act polite and, explaining where the others are, I lead her into the living room.

"That's all right." She smiles as she sits on the sofa, but her eyes are sad. "I got here a little earlier than I expected. But I was actually hoping to talk to *you*, Kiera."

"Me?" I can hardly believe it. Grandma Josephson has never been terribly interested in me. Well, besides reminding me to stand or sit straight or brush my messy hair, something that's pointless now. Hannah was always her favorite…and Maddie gets special favor too, probably because she's the baby. I study my grandmother with suspicion. Why did she want to talk to me? Had my mom told her what a mess I've become?

"I had lunch with some girl friends over in Crestview. Our friend Val Peterson mentioned that she was recently hired by the park and recreation district, right here in your town."

I nod as if I'm interested, but I'm actually trying to think of an excuse to escape this unwanted chitchat session. Why on earth does Grandma think I care about her old lady friends?

"So anyway, Val's heading up the whole park district. And I got to thinking that she might be a good resource for you, Kiera."

"A resource for what?" Did my grandmother want to send me to day camp or sign me up for tap-dance classes?

"A job. Your mom told me you're looking for a summer job. So I told Val about you, and she thinks she might have a job opening. She's invited you to come in for an interview on Monday morning. I hope you don't mind that I made you an appointment for ten o'clock. Here's her phone number." She holds up her cell phone and starts rattling off a number. "Although you don't need to call. Just go in and talk to Val." She smiles triumphantly as I plug the number into my phone, and I act like I plan to follow up on this, but actually I think my grandma is slightly nuts.

"I know, I know." Grandma gives me a sheepish smile. "Your grandfather, God bless his soul, used to say that I was an awful busybody. Always interfering. But I like to think that I'm just being helpful." She reaches over to ruffle my hair, like I'm about six years old. "You don't mind, do you?"

"I guess not. It probably wouldn't hurt for me to go in to talk to her." I try to sound respectful and polite. "But I did put applications in at restaurants and I'd hoped—"

"Oh, you don't want to work in a restaurant, Kiera. Goodness knows you've never been much use in a kitchen." She laughed then grew somber. "Not like our Hannah was." She sighed. "Oh, my, I still remember that birthday cake she made for my last birthday. Lemon chiffon—from scratch, too. That child could cook."

I don't know why, but this makes me want to scream. Instead, I dig my fingernails into my palms and silently count to ten. Why do all conversations with our family eventually wind up back here? Hannah. She's been gone almost six months and yet she is still here—it's like she inhabits everything and she is everywhere. Almost even more so than when she was actually alive. Sometimes it feels like Hannah is haunting us—or maybe she's *taunting* us. Reminding us of what we've lost. Or more likely she's reminding us of the parts we all played, the responsibilities we bear in her demise. It's like it'll never end.

"Maddie said she wants to learn to cook this summer," my grandmother drones on in an absent way, clearly changing the subject in an attempt to fill the dead air space. "I told Maddie we would start with chocolate chip cookies and then move on to ginger—"

To my relief, she is interrupted by Maddie entering the

house. My little sister lets out a happy shriek and, dropping her backpack by the door, rushes over to hug Grandma. Feeling released from my social responsibility, I make an excuse to return to my room, leaving Maddie to take over. After all, our grandmother is here for her, not me. Let Maddie play Miss Congeniality now.

In my room, I'm tempted to pull out Hannah's diary again, but it makes me uncomfortable knowing that Maddie and Grandma are in the house. I can't imagine how awkward it would be for one of them to discover me reading the private book. So I go over to my window and, feeling like a caged animal, I look out across the side yard. Yesterday was the last day of school, and already I'm restless and bored and just plain unhappy. How will I make it through an entire summer?

Across the street I notice movement in the neighbor's front yard. Mrs. Baxter is wrapping black and orange streamers around the lampposts alongside their driveway, twisting them round and round like orange and black candy canes. Does she think it's Halloween? Then it hits me—those are our high school colors! *Tonight is graduation night!* Mrs. Baxter is getting their house ready for a graduation party for their daughter Nora. The Baxter family and friends will be joyously celebrating the night away.

Meanwhile the Josephsons will be over here...*not* celebrating. I can just imagine the lapses of uncomfortable silence as we sit around the long dining room table, everyone trying not to think about or mention that Hannah's senior class is marching through the gymnasium, making hypocritical speeches, collecting diplomas, throwing hats in the air…and that Hannah isn't there among them. Her big night that she'd so looked forward to will proceed merrily along without her. And now it's useless—I can't hold back my tears any longer.

Four

I DON'T THINK ANYONE OBSERVED ME sneak out the backdoor. But as I streak across the yard and climb up into the tree house, I feel it's vital to remain unseen. If I could choose a superpower, it would probably be invisibility. I realize it's childish to think about superpowers at my age. But so is hiding out up here. Not that I care.

As I pull the warped plywood door shut, I remember how Dad and Grandpa helped Hannah and me to build this structure, back when Maddie was a baby. Hopefully it won't collapse now. I haven't been up here in a few years, but I don't remember the ceiling being this low. As I crouch like a hunchback, using a sweatshirt from my backpack to sweep out cobwebs and several years' accumulation of dead leaves and dirt, I vaguely wonder if this space could've shrunk.

It had been my idea to make a tree house in the maple tree. I started my campaign by presenting Dad with some pictures I'd collected, insisting that it was his responsibility as our dad to build a tree house. But he always claimed he was too busy with work and life and, of course, his Saturday golf. In my dad's defense, he didn't know a hammer from a saw, but when Hannah joined forces with me, turning on her blue-eyed blonde charm, Dad finally conceded. Unfortunately it didn't take long before he proved his carpentry ineptness to us, followed up by a visit to the emergency room and about twelve stitches in his left hand. Thanks to Grandpa Josephson, the tree house was eventually finished. For several years, Hannah and I happily occupied this space, but she eventually started acting like a teenager, preferring her bedroom and adolescent friends to her little sister. Without her company, the tree house slowly became a lonely place, losing its appeal for me.

I couldn't even entice Maddie to scale the rope-and-board ladder by then. But it was my own fault that she had no interest. My little sister had been about four when we went to the Grand Canyon and suffered a slight meltdown. Later on Mom claimed Maddie had acrophobia, which actually means fear of heights but I thought meant spiders (I later learned that was arachnophobia). But wanting to keep the tree house for just Hannah and me, I told

Maddie all about poisonous spiders, even showing her photos of a black widow and brown recluse, and claiming I'd spotted some of these creepy critters in the shadowy corners of the tree house. Thanks to me, Maddie probably has both acrophobia and arachnophobia now. Poor kid.

I give the tree house one more swipe with my hoody and then, satisfied that I've spooked any unwanted inhabitants out, I settle into a corner of the old shag carpet and extract Hannah's diary from my backpack. I open the book but am distracted by the Baxters' party decorations. Even through the foggy window, I can see Mrs. Baxter tying helium-filled orange and black balloons along the picket fence in the front yard. She's obviously pulling out all the stops for Nora's celebration tonight. Nice for Nora. Not so much for us. So instead of reading the diary like I planned, I pull out my phone and dial Dad's number. I can tell by his curt answer that he's still playing golf.

"I know you don't like me to interrupt your golf," I begin carefully.

"What's wrong?" he asks with concern. "Is everyone okay?"

I quickly reassure him then explain about the Baxters and graduation night.

"Oh?" He sounds slightly confused...and bothered.

"I just thought you'd want to know," I say defensively. "I mean, because Grandma is here and Mom was fixing dinner tonight and, you know, we'll be in the dining room where we'll be sure to witness all the festivities across the street." I describe the gaudy decorations now. "It might be hard, you know?"

"What am I supposed to do about it?" His tone is edgy now. He's clearly aggravated that I've involved him in something he'd rather pretend doesn't exist.

"I don't know. I was just giving you a head's up. Sorry to interrupt your—"

"Do you think I should take everyone out for dinner?" His tone is slightly gentler now, more like the old Dad. "We could avoid the Baxters altogether?"

"Yeah. That might help."

"Fine. Tell your mom that I'll be home by—"

"No, Dad. You'll need to tell her yourself." I want to add that Mom never listens to me anyway, but I know that will simply irritate him more.

"Fine," he snapped. "I'll call her after I finish this hole."

"Have a good game," I say without enthusiasm. As I hang up, tossing my phone back into my bag, I wonder why I bothered to call him—does it even matter? It's not like we can keep avoiding everything forever. Or maybe we can.

I shove the guilt down inside of me as I open the diary again. Rationalizing that, as the bereaved sister, I have a right to read Hannah's diary. I even pretend that she would agree, as if giving me permission. The next two entries continue similar to the first one. Hannah was unhappy with her life...and unhappy pretending like she wasn't unhappy. In some ways she seemed to be trapped. Like she'd created this candy-coated image for herself—and suddenly realized that the sweetness was gagging her. I wasn't too surprised to read the entry about how she'd broken up with Wyatt, but I was a little surprised to learn what she did afterward.

> *February 3*
> *I cannot believe what I did last night. I'm not even sure I want to write it down today. Except that I need to get the words out—and examine them by the light of day. I'll just have to be sure to hide my diary in a good spot when I'm done. Which doesn't quite make sense—I mean didn't I want everyone to know that I'm not who they think I am? So confused.*
>
> *So, even though it's been a few weeks, Wyatt is still in denial about our breakup. He even told Haley that he's certain I'll change my mind and realize what a catch he is and come crawling back—and in time for prom too. Ha!*
>
> *Well, for some reason that just irks me. It's not that I hate Wyatt. I don't. But he is a bit arrogant. A bit too full of himself. Besides that, he is boring and predictable. And I have no intention of getting back together with him. So, to prove my point, I started flirting with Maxwell Harter earlier this week. And, yes, I'm fully aware that Maxwell is a "bad boy." A very good looking bad boy, I might*

add. But I decided Maxwell is exactly what I need—a perfect way to exit my role of Polly-Hannah for good.

I wasn't too surprised when Maxwell asked me out. The way he asked was more like a challenge. He actually said that he knew I'd never go out with someone like him. Well, I jumped for the bait. And when he said he wanted to take me to a party, I acted like that was perfectly fine. I didn't question what kind of party—because I already knew that a party wasn't considered a party for someone like Maxwell if alcohol wasn't flowing freely. I was a bit surprised when I discovered that kids were smoking weed there as well. Especially since some of them, like Maxwell, are jocks and our school has a zero tolerance drug policy. Anyway I tried to act totally natural. Like I was cool with the whole thing. And when some of them teased me, even calling me "Little Goody Two Shoes," which made me want to scream, I just turned it into a joke. At my expense.

Although I passed on the weed, I went ahead and drank some beer. At the time, I promised myself that if Maxwell got too drunk to drive, I would definitely call home for a ride—although I didn't really want to do that. Anyway, Maxwell could tell I didn't like the taste of the beer so he made me a drink with some fruit juice with some kind of alcohol in it, and I got that down with no problem.

And here's the really weird part—I liked it! I felt so free and happy—like I'd really escaped Polly-Hannah and all the responsibility that goes with that label. I danced with Maxwell. And, yes, we made out. But I did manage to draw the line on doing more than that—even though he was very persistent. But I told him it was our first date—and to just get over himself. Fortunately he did.

But here's what's so unnerving...I barely remember him bringing me home last night. And I have no idea if he was sober enough to drive safely. That bothers me a lot! Thankfully, I don't think my parents were still up when I slipped in late. That's one of the perks of being the "good daughter." They trust me. But if they had any idea what I'd been up to last night—well, they would be shocked.

In fact, I feel a little shocked right now. And ashamed. I'm ashamed that I let Maxwell drive me home when I suspect that he was intoxicated. I'm also ashamed that I can't fully remember it. But I do remember having fun. So now I feel just plain confused.

I'm not sure I'll ever do that again. I know Wyatt would freak if he knew. And Haley would probably disown me. Hopefully they won't find out, although I'm sure it'll be all over school by

Monday. Oh, I wish I didn't care. I wish I could
be like Maxwell and his friends. And yet...I don't.
Here's the honest truth, I really don't know how I
feel anymore. It's like I've crossed some invisible
line. What if I can't go back?

As I close the diary, I am dumbfounded. I cannot believe my goody-goody sister did something like that—
and I never even suspected it! I honestly had no idea she'd
been into partying. My parents didn't either. Hannah
was always the perfect angel, the golden girl. How was it
possible she'd gone out with someone like Maxwell Harter—and that I'd been totally clueless about it? To be fair,
I was only fourteen at the time and probably caught up
in my own personal drama, which included making my
own decisions about drinking and partying—ones that I
never dreamed of telling my sister or anyone in my family
about. But I'd never dreamed that perfect Hannah had tip-
toed over that line herself. And, even though she's gone,
it makes me really uncomfortable to think of Hannah in
this different light. And yet it's strangely reassuring too.
I can't even wrap my head around it. But I want to know
more.

I'm about to start reading again, but I hear someone
calling my name. Of course, it's my mom. I didn't realize
she was home already. But she does not sound happy as
she yells for me. I stay low, hoping she doesn't suspect I'm
up here. And when she finally stops calling my name and

I'm certain she's gone back into the house, I slip down the ladder and am just going through the backdoor when I nearly knock into her.

"Where have you been?" she demands. "You knew your grandmother was coming and all I asked you to do was—"

"I did *everything* you said," I insist. "Why are you in such a snit?"

Her blue eyes flash angrily as she points to the sink. "Look at that mess."

I peer down to see the pan I removed from the stove, the potatoes still soaking in water. "So?"

"You honestly think I can make potato salad out of that muck?"

I shrug. "I really don't know."

"You are absolutely hopeless, Kiera. Why I ever imagined I could count on—"

"Oh, there you are," my grandmother says cheerfully. "I thought I heard voices in here."

We both turn to look at her, and I can tell by her expression that she's heard more than my mother would like.

"Is something wrong?" Grandma asks innocently.

Mom forces a tolerant smile. "No, no…I just forgot that Kiera is rather useless in the kitchen."

Grandma laughs as she slips a comforting arm around my waist. "Well, I thought that was an established fact." She gently pokes me in the ribs. "And I meant to say something earlier, Kiera, but you could really use some meat on your bones. Perhaps you really should be spending more time in the kitchen. I could give you my easy-breezy fudge recipe. All it takes is a microwave and a strong stirring arm."

"Sounds good," I say meekly.

"Well, this is just great." Mom groans as she drains the water from the potatoes. Then she gives up, dumping the pale glop into the sink with a splat. "So much for the potato salad I planned for dinner tonight."

"Didn't Dad call you?" I ask with hesitation.

"Why would Dad call?" Mom narrows her eyes.

"I, uh, well, I talked to him a little bit ago. He said he was going to call you."

"Isn't Alex golfing today?" Grandma frowns as Mom pushes the mess down the garbage disposal.

"Yes, he's returned to his *usual* Saturday routine." Mom's tone is sharper than normal—for Grandma, that is.

Fighting back irritation at my dad for not doing as promised—*again*—I decide to take this bull by the horns. "Dad wants to take us all to dinner tonight," I announce brightly. "I think he's already made reservations, but he must've gotten busy and—"

"He never mentioned any of this to me earlier." Mom glares at me, seemingly oblivious to Grandma now.

"Oh, it's not necessary to go out for dinner just because I'm here." Grandma glances around the kitchen as if looking for something she could whip into a meal. "I'm sure we can—"

"No," I say stubbornly. "Dad *wants* to take everyone out. He told me to tell you not to bother with dinner, Mom."

Mom still looks skeptical, and I know she's mad at me, but at least she stops questioning me. With my phone in hand, I wander out of the kitchen, pausing in the dining room to quickly text my dad a reminder to make reservations—and call Mom.

"I told Maddie to gather up whatever she's taking with her," Grandma says as she and Mom come through the dining room together. "I want it all packed into my trunk tonight so we can leave first thing in the morning. I'd like to be home in time for church tomorrow since I'm in charge of—"

"*What on earth?*" Mom's voice has a high pitch, and I realize she's at the dining room window—staring at the Baxters' house.

"That's interesting." Grandma joins her. "A bit early for Halloween, isn't it?"

"That is not..." Mom's hand covers her mouth. "For Halloween."

"Maybe it's a birthday?" Grandma tries.

"It's graduation night," I quietly tell Grandma. "At the high school."

"Oh my..." Grandma's brow creases with realization.

"It's for Nora Baxter, across the street. She's graduating tonight."

"Ex—excuse me." Mom's voice cracks as she backs

away from the window. I notice her hands are trembling, a signal she's about to have a meltdown. Not that I blame her since I felt pretty much the same way.

"Yes." Grandma nods sadly. "Yes, yes…I understand."

"Come on." I link my arm in Grandma's as my mom scurries away. "Let's go back to the kitchen, and you can tell me all about making fudge. Maybe we can make some to have later on tonight."

Grandma looks doubtful, she but allows me to lead her back to the kitchen where I make a pretense of looking through drawers and cabinets, as if I have the slightest clue of what's involved in fudge making. Meanwhile, I know Mom has sequestered herself in her room to cry. As I set a mixing bowl and measuring cups on the counter, just like Hannah used to do, I wish that I didn't care. I've made it my mission *not to care* and sometimes I think I've actually accomplished it, but then I get blindsided… by my own heart.

Five

MORE THAN ANYTHING, MOIRA WISHED this day was over and done with—and that she could escape by going to bed with a sleeping pill or two. She opened her medicine cabinet and removed her Xanax prescription, gazing fondly at the familiar bottle. And it was half full too. It had been nearly a month since she'd taken one of these, and she'd promised herself that she would throw out the rest of the pills. But she hadn't. She tried to tell herself that she'd simply forgotten, but she knew that wasn't true. She wasn't that forgetful.

Although she had somehow managed to forget that tonight was graduation night. Not to mention she'd brilliantly suggested that Virginia pick up Maddie today. And she'd planned for a family dinner in the dining room tonight—across from the neighbors who would be celebrating their daughter's graduation. What was she thinking? Obviously, she *wasn't* thinking. What else was new?

She opened the bottle and shook a pale blue pill into her still-trembling palm. Such a soothing shade of blue, like a promise of peace, tranquility…escape. She popped it into her mouth and washed it down with lukewarm tap water. Taking a single pill did not mean she was going to become an addict. Not that she'd been addicted before. She'd simply become a little too dependent. But her daughter was dead—what better excuse did one need to rely on a mind-dulling pill? It was prescribed by her doctor. It took the edge off and allowed her to function. What was the harm of that?

The text tone sounded on her phone, reminding her that she had responsibilities. Virginia was still here. In the kitchen with Kiera—which was almost funny. And she needed to be sure that Maddie packed everything she needed. She picked up her phone to see it was from Alex— announcing that he'd made a reservation to take all the ladies to dinner tonight. Did Alex remember that it was graduation night too? Had he thought about the house across the street? If so, that was surprisingly thoughtful— albeit slightly out of character. Well, out of character *now*. He used to be thoughtful. But no one was the same as before anymore. As far as Moira could see, no one would ever be the same again. Nothing would.

She texted him back, and he promised to be home in time to shower and change. As she tossed her phone into her bag, she wished for something more. But *what*? To turn back the clock? That was impossible. But just the same, she wished it.

By the time she returned to the kitchen, she felt a bit more at ease. But seeing Virginia and Kiera creating what looked like a ridiculous mess, she instantly felt like backing out and running the other way. Instead, she opened the bottle of wine that she'd been chilling and had planned to serve with dinner. Without saying a word to anyone, she poured two glasses, handing one to Virginia.

"Oh, my." Virginia's brows arched. "What's this?"

"Happy hour." Moira forced a smile. "Alex will be home soon, he can join us if he wants. Then we'll leave for dinner around 6:30."

Virginia's smile looked slightly nervous, but she held up her glass like a toast. "To better days?" she said tentatively.

"Yes." Moira clinked her glass against Virginia's. "To better days." As if that were possible, but at least they could pretend. She sat down at the breakfast bar, looking at Kiera, who seemed to be intently stirring something in a mixing bowl. "What goes on here?"

"I'm teaching Kiera to make my easy-breezy fudge," Virginia said with pride. "And I think perhaps there is hope for her after all."

Kiera gave Moira a glance which suggested otherwise but said nothing. Moira took another sip. And, yes, she knew that combining Xanax with wine was a no-no, but she did not care. Besides, no one else knew what she'd done. And she wouldn't be driving tonight. If this little self-med combo helped her make it through the evening, well, why should anyone care?

She made small talk with Virginia for a bit, trying to appear calm and relaxed and social, then eventually excused herself to check on Maddie. "I want to make sure she packs her allergy medication."

"Make sure she brings her EpiPen."

"Yes." Moira nodded. "And all her dental care products. Those braces will not clean themselves." Of course, Moira had no doubts that her hyper efficient twelve-year-old would already have it together, but it was a good excuse to escape Kiera's messy cooking experiment.

Maddie was just zipping a bag closed when Moira went into her room. As usual, Maddie's room was tidy albeit slightly stark. But Moira knew that was how Maddie liked it. And thanks to her allergies, it was for the best. Maddie's most interesting furniture item was her bookshelf filled with all of her beloved books, although it appeared that some had been removed. "Did you pack books to take to Grandma's?" Moira asked.

"Just a few of my favorites." Maddie shrugged. "You know, like *Harry Potter*, and *Narnia* and *The Hobbit*. Sometimes I like to read them again."

"Do you need help getting your things down to Grandma's car?" Moira glanced around.

"Nope. This is the last bag. Well, except for my backpack, but I'll take that out tomorrow."

Although she suspected it was unnecessary, Moira quizzed Maddie on any little things she might've forgotten, but not surprisingly, Maddie had it all covered. Moira gave her a little hug. "You're such an organized girl. So mature for your age. I appreciate that."

"Thanks." Maddie's smile looked a little sad.

Moira studied her. "You're really okay with this? You do want to spend the summer with Grandma, don't you?"

"Yeah, it'll be fun. Grandma has all kinds of stuff planned for us."

"You won't miss your friends here in town?"

"Olivia is going to be gone most of the summer anyway," Maddie reminded her. "And we'll keep in touch online. Besides, Kendall will be at Grandma's a lot too." Maddie smiled. "That'll be fun."

"Right." Moira nodded. Maddie's ten-year-old cousin was one of the few people that looked up to Maddie. She would be company this summer. Moira waved her finger at Maddie's shorts and t-shirt. "Dad's taking us all out to dinner. You suppose you could put on something a little more festive?"

Maddie's mouth twisted to one side. "I guess so."

"Thanks, honey." Moira ran her hand through Maddie's sandy curls. She wished that Maddie's hair could stay light, but she could tell it was getting darker. Hannah had been the only natural blonde in the family. Well, besides Moira. Although, as Moira's hairdresser had pointed out, her roots were getting grayer all the time.

Moira studied Maddie for a long moment. She didn't like to think of her daughter as an ugly duckling, but Maddie was definitely in an awkward stage right now. But perhaps she would grow into a swan someday. Although she would never be as beautiful as Hannah—that was too much to hope for.

As Moira left Maddie's room, she felt guilty for comparing her daughters. She'd never admit to it, but she knew she'd always secretly done so. Hannah had been so delightful—right from the beginning too. She'd never had an awkward stage. Hannah had always been so pretty, so sweet, so talented, so perfect. A hard act for her sisters to follow, for sure. But that act had ended in January. The curtain had fallen and the audience had gone home. Sometimes it felt like Moira was the only one left…silently applauding her daughter in a lonely dark auditorium.

Six

I FEEL LIKE I'VE SACRIFICED MYSELF AS I stare at the menu in the busy restaurant. Was this really my idea? Everyone knows I hate going out to eat with my family. It's like being stuck in a public torture chamber. And it doesn't help that my grandmother is here to witness it. So I'm determined to be on my best behavior. If it falls apart, they won't be able to blame me...I hope.

Unfortunately, this restaurant doesn't have a single vegan dish—and the waiter is waiting with an impatient expression. I know if I make the slightest stink about the menu's lack of options, my mom will flip out. And even when I order the chef salad, asking them to hold all the non-vegan items, she rolls her eyes.

"You might as well get a side salad," she tells me as she hands her menu to the waiter.

"Fine," I say. "I'll have the side salad."

The waiter looks dismayed. "That's all?"

"And a side of fries," I add, hoping that'll smooth this over.

"Fries?" Mom looks at me like I've just ordered arsenic.

"Fine," I say tersely. "No fries."

"Oh, let her get fries," Grandma insists. "Might put some meat on her bones."

"Or zits on her face," Mom says quietly.

"Moira," Dad says with disapproval. He hates it when anyone makes a scene in a restaurant. My mom used to hate it too, but it doesn't seem like she cares tonight.

Mom scowls at him. "If Kiera would just eat healthily, she might actually—"

"Vegan *is* healthy," I protest. "But this restaurant doesn't have—"

"That's enough." Dad gives me a warning look, and I know it's time to zip it.

After the waiter leaves, Grandma attempts to make small talk. She rambles on about the new house that Uncle Bart and Aunt Jenny are building this summer. "Their other house sold so fast that they had to rent a tiny one-bedroom apartment," she says. "That's why Kendall will be spending a lot of time at my house. Won't be so crowded in the apartment."

"I can't wait to see Kendall." Maddie sounds almost happy, which makes me feel better.

"She's excited about seeing you too," Grandma reassures her. "Making big plans."

I watch as the waiter sets down our drinks. Sodas for Maddie and me. Iced tea for Grandma. But both my parents ordered "adult beverages." It's weird because they never drank much alcohol before. Never at a family dinner in a restaurant. The most they imbibed in was an occasional champagne for some celebration. Or spiked eggnog at Christmas. But after Hannah died, Mom started drinking more wine. And Dad acquired a taste for craft beers.

I was surprised when Mom ordered wine with dinner, since she already had some at home. But I realize the whole business about graduation night is stressful—for everyone. Even so—and there's no way I can tell my mother this—alcohol does *not* bring out her best side. And she's already been more irritable than usual—especially considering that Grandma is here to witness it. But, hey, it's her life. If she wants to derail it, who am I to try to stop her? And Dad apparently doesn't know that she's already had some wine. Whatever.

Dad talks briefly about his golf game, giving us an update on his golf buddies, not that any of us have much interest in it, but at least it fills some of the dead air. Then Grandma tells them about her friend Val Peterson and how I'm going in for a job interview on Monday.

"That's great," Dad tells his mom. "Like I always say, it's not what you know, but who you know."

I bristle at what feels like a slam. "Well, I put applications in at several restaurants," I say with more confidence than I feel. "I'm hoping Leonardi's will call."

Mom laughs in a snotty way. "Leonardi's? Seriously, Kiera, you think you could get hired *there*? Let me guess, did you go in there dressed like *that*?"

"They have uniforms, you know."

"What about your hair?" she demands in a voice that's a bit loud.

"I like her hair," Maddie says. "It's cool."

I blink in surprise. "Really?"

"Maddie's just being nice," Mom says sharply.

"What about this restaurant?" Grandma says, obviously trying to change the subject. "It seems a nice place to work."

"Except they don't have anything *vegan* on the menu," Mom says in snarky tone. "Kiera wouldn't like that." She takes a big sip of her Merlot.

I press my lips tightly together, silently counting to ten.

"But back to the parks and rec job." Dad turns to his mother with a desperate frown, like he can see his dinner-boat slowly sinking and wants someone to throw him a life preserver. "Do you think Kiera would really have a chance?"

"Not if she goes in there dressed like a bum." Mom grimly shakes her head. "They say you should dress for the life you want—I think Kiera wants to be homeless." She laughs again, like this is real funny.

"*Moira,*" Dad says sharply.

"Excuse me." I clumsily stand, tossing my napkin on the table. "I *would* like to be homeless, Mom. It'd be lots better than *this.*" And then I turn away and head straight for the door. I can hear my dad protesting, but it's too late. Angry tears are burning in my eyes, and I refuse to sit there sobbing over my stupid side salad and fries while my mom continues to jab at me. As soon as I'm out of the restaurant, I take off in a fast sprint. I'm tempted to go in the opposite direction of my house, but I'm not really ready to be homeless. Not yet. As I run, I get a better plan. I'll hole up in the tree house.

I run all the way home and then breathlessly gather up all the things I think I'll need for a somewhat comfortable night of camping and, after several trips, I am set. I have food and flashlight and bedding and my phone, which already has several texts from Dad.

Oh, I'll let him know I'm okay before long. It's not that I want to worry them. At least not Dad and Grandma and Maddie. I couldn't care less if Mom was worried. The problem is she won't be. She'd be relieved if I disappeared for good. I know for a fact that if a genie popped out of her Merlot bottle and gave her one wish, my mother would exchange my life for Hannah's. In a heartbeat! I'd be dead and buried and Hannah would still be here. And everyone would be a lot happier.

It would be easy to sit up here and have a nice little pity party, but the truth is I'm glad Mom gave me an excuse to escape family night at the restaurant. And there's some satisfaction in knowing that the rest of my family felt a tiny bit sorry for me. Besides that, I'm eager to get back to Hannah's diary. But first I text Dad, assuring him that I didn't go jump off a bridge. Then I turn off my phone and open my dead sister's diary.

The next few pages bounce around a bit. On one page she is full of remorse for her wild night of partying with Max. But the next page, she is considering going out with him again. Her best friend Haley can't believe it and thinks Hannah has lost her mind. Even Wyatt is warning her to be careful. But, at the same time, Max is giving her lots of attention as he entices her into his exciting world.

I'm so curious about where this is going that I read quickly, flipping pages until I can see that two weeks and two crazy weekend dates with Max have passed. It's hard to believe that no one in our family was aware of what Hannah was up to in the winter of her junior year. But according to her diary, she's gone to great lengths to make her family think she's still dating Wyatt—and yet she's about to go on her third date with Max. But something is weird here—it looks like a couple of pages have been torn out of her diary. I eagerly go to the next entry and can tell that something dramatic happened—something that was written in the missing pages...and removed.

I'm so ashamed. And angry. Humiliated and enraged. And even though I just wrote about the whole horrible night, I can't stand to see those words in writing. And the thought of anyone else reading those horrible words is really disturbing. I either need to remove them from this book or just burn the whole stupid thing. Except that it seems to help to write about the ordeal. Kind of like therapy. Man, do I need some therapy now.

I hate Max. Hate, hate, hate him! He is the devil. I can't believe I fell for his lies. I can't believe I trusted him. I can't believe I walked away from someone like Wyatt to get involved with someone like Max. Haley was right. I am crazy. Why didn't I listen to her? Why didn't I believe Wyatt when he said Max was a user and a loser? Why am I so stupid?

As much as I hate Max…I hate myself too. I feel dirty and ruined. And there's no one I can talk to about this. Mom would be so disappointed in me, I could never go to her. Dad would probably get angry. He might even try to hurt Max. Or call the police. Max is eighteen and I'm only sixteen. At the very least that is statutory rape in our state.

But what if my suspicions are right? What if that lowlife slipped something into my drink? That's way, way worse! But it makes sense. Because I've never felt like that before, so disconnected from everything . . . and then it all just blurred together. How could that happen after one single drink? I know that punch was heavily laced with

alcohol, but how could it have wiped me out like
that? And if Max slipped me a roofie—I hate him
even more. I wish he were dead!

I stop reading—trying to process these words. I cannot
believe it! This is not like my sister—not at all. It's like I'm
reading about someone else. No way would Hannah be
involved in something like this. It just doesn't fit. Does
not compute! This is not the Hannah I knew. And how
was it possible she kept something this big from all of us?
I don't get it.

I'm in such denial that I go back and reread that last
section again. And when I finish I'm convinced that Max
Harter must've forced himself on Hannah. And, I'm not
expert on the law, but that wouldn't be just statutory. If
she was too doped to give consent, that was just plain rape.
And I know that's against the law. Part of me is tempted
to run out and find Dad—to tell him what happened and
show him her diary and beg him to go to the police and
press charges against the creep.

I realize that Max Harter must be nineteen by now,
doing who knows what—and maybe getting away with
it. Seriously, I wouldn't care if charges of rape destroyed
his life. He deserves it! Didn't he essentially destroy my
sister's life? Isn't that what she's saying in her diary? I'm
sure this little blue book could be used as evidence in a
court of law. And I would so love to see that lowlife Max
Harter fully prosecuted! I'd like to see him squirming in

court, and his face plastered all over the media as a heart-less rapist. Especially when the news revealed that his victim died tragically, less than a year later.

And yet, somehow I don't think that's what Hannah would want. Oh, I'm sure she wouldn't mind seeing the creep behind bars. Who wouldn't? But I remember her memorial service...the crowded church and the way everyone remembered Hannah as a girl who was so good and pure, so kind and sweet. The phrase "like an angel" was flung around a lot. To bring her diary to light now—even in an attempt to prosecute Max Harter the jerk—would drag Hannah's name through the mud right along with his. If she felt ruined then, how much worse would it be to ruin her memory too? I'm too confused to sort this out right now, so I return to the section, finishing it off.

> *I'm so desperate, I actually considered confiding to Kiera today. I even started to say something, but then she went and picked another fight with me, teasing me for being such a neat-freak simply because I'd complained about the mess she left in our shared bathroom over the weekend. She's such a slob when it comes to hygiene and housekeeping. She always claims I'm obsessed with cleanliness. And maybe I am today. I feel so filthy and dirty. Like I will never be clean again.*

As I close the book, I feel a huge load of guilt burying

me. I'm pretty sure I remember that day. It was a Sunday, and our parents had taken Maddie somewhere. Hannah had complained about a pile of dirty clothes I'd left in the bathroom and a few other things. Then later on she came to my room, wanting to talk to me. Her expression looked so sour that I assumed I was about to get another lecture on cleaning, so I'd gone off on her before she could even start. And it had turned into one of our worst fights ever—yelling and screaming and slamming doors. And I actually felt victorious when I finally drove my beautiful picture-perfect sister to tears. Like she'd deserved it.

This is a heavy, heavy load to bear, and I find myself wishing that I'd never stolen her diary. Besides feeling like a heartless monster, I have opened a huge can of worms. I mean, what am I supposed to do with this information about Max? Tell my parents? I don't think so. And it's something I'd never want Maddie to know. But to keep it to myself feels too hard. And yet I know that's what I'll have to do. At least for now. I can't even force myself to read another word. I start to put the diary back into my pack, but that feels unsafe. What if someone found it?

I feel like I should destroy this book before anyone else has a chance to read it. Should I burn it or something? Maybe, for Hannah's sake. But I'm in this deep…I know I can't burn it without reading the rest of it. And there's no way I can read the rest of it tonight. I already feel sick over having read what I've read. Sick and guilty.

In the meantime, I need a secure place to hide it. Suddenly I remember the loose board on the window sill, which reminds me of the time I snuck a pornographic magazine up here. My friend Carrie and I had discovered the contraband in her older brother's bedroom. We brought it up to the tree house to examine in private. Of course, we were both disgusted—and slightly confused by the photos. And hearing Hannah coming up the ladder, I'd stuffed the nasty rag down beneath the loose window sill. Of course, our nervous fits of giggling clued Hannah in, and before long we were showing her the dirty magazine. Hannah stepped right into her big sister role, insisting we needed to dispose of it—and so the three of us tore it apart and ceremoniously burned it in the backyard fire pit. I think we were all glad to see it going up in flames.

Feeling that Hannah would approve, I pull up the loose board then slide her diary into the space inside the wall. I securely pound the window sill back into place and take a deep breath. I clearly did not know my sister as well as I thought I did. It feels truly awful to realize how horrid I was to her right when she needed me. But I remember that was the same time I started getting into my bad girl image. I'm sure that was all related to sibling jealousy. About the same time I started calling her *Polly-Hannah* and *Goody Two Shoes*. Acting like being a nice person was a bad thing. No wonder she never confided in me. I actually ache inside to realize that I was such a pathetic excuse of a sister.

Seven

MOIRA KNEW SHE'D STEPPED OVER A LINE, but by the time she and Alex were going head-to-head in the master bedroom, she couldn't remember exactly what she'd said or done. "Stop picking on me." She shook her finger in his face. "I'm forced to watch the neighbors celebrating their daughter's graduation tonight—and *my daughter is dead!*" Moira heard the slur in her raised voice—*celebrating* had come out more like *shelebrating*—and knew she'd had too much wine… along with that pill. The Xanax was supposed to relax her, to take the edge off. Yet here she was yelling—and she wanted to throw things!

"She was *my* daughter too!" Alex kicked off a shoe.

"Yes, but you weren't close to her like I was, Alex." She tried to soften her words now, hoping for a small measure of sympathy. Maybe she would tell him about going up to the cemetery today. "Hannah was more than a daughter. She was my friend and I miss her dearly—Hannah was my best friend, and she's gone!"

"There's nothing we can do about that," he calmly declared. "We just have to move on with our lives. It's been six months and—"

"It *hasn't* been six months!" she screamed at him. "It's only been *five* months and two weeks! Five and a half stinking, crappy, horrible months! Five and a half hideous, never-ending—"

"Keep it down," Alex commanded. "My mom's going to hear you in the guest room, and she's already been through enough tonight."

"I don't care who hears me!" She felt herself growing louder. "I have every right to be angry. My daughter is dead! Hannah is never coming home and—"

"You have *two other daughters*." Alex glared at her. "Not that anyone would notice. You're shipping Maddie off and you treat Kiera like dirt."

"They're *your* daughters too," she yelled back. "Not that anyone would notice!"

"But you're their *mother*, Moira. And they need a mother right now. Even my mom could see you're not handling it—"

"Not *handling* it?" she shrieked. "I'm still here, aren't I? And tell me, just how am I *supposed* to handle it? My daughter should've been graduating with her friends tonight, Alex. We should've been there watching her, celebrating with her. Instead we go out for a lousy dinner at a lousy restaurant and everyone treats me like I'm the enemy! I am *not* the enemy! I am not—"

"But you *are* their mother!"

"And *you* are their *father!* Do not lecture me, Alexander Josephson. You're never here for the girls anymore. You're not here for anyone anymore. You checked out when Hannah died." She shook her fist in his face. *"You're gone. Just as gone as Hannah. Do you hear me? You're not here* anymore!"

He tapped his chest. "Look at me, Moira. I'm still here. I came home tonight. I tried to take you and the ladies out for—"

"And what a *wonderful* evening we had." She wanted to be sarcastic, to cut into him, to hurt him. Didn't he deserve it? "Such a lovely evening! Kiera makes an ugly scene, and you defend her. Maddie clams up, and you blame me. And then your mother talks nonstop about people I've never even heard of, and you—"

"So you don't take any responsibility for tonight?" His angry face got so close she felt worried. "You make *Mommy Dearest* look good, Moira."

She narrowed her eyes. "Is that any worse than being a deadbeat dad?"

"Deadbeat dad?" His eyes flashed. "Are you kidding? I work my tail off providing for this—"

"Oh, don't pretend that you don't love escaping to

your work. And when you're not escaping in your fancy executive suite, you're off playing golf or going to a ballgame with your buddies. Oh, you say you're with clients, but I know the truth. You're just doing anything you can to avoid coming home!"

"Can you blame me if I don't want to come home?" Now he shook his own fist in the air. "My wife has turned into a total lush. And, let me tell you, you're an angry, mean-spirited drunk, Moira. Just like you said your mother used to be! Remember how much you hated it? Well, you are turning into your mother." He was putting his shoes back on now. "Tell me, why should I want to be around for *that*?"

"Then why don't you just leave?"

"That's the best idea you've had in months."

"Just pack your bags and go! Who needs you?"

"That's just what I plan to do."

"Run away," she taunted. "You're such a coward."

"*I'm* a coward? You're the one hiding in the bottle."

"You're the one running away," she yelled back. "And I know why too."

He put his hands on his hips, giving her that look— that *I'm so much more mature than you* look that he knew she hated. "Why?" he asked in a flat tone.

"Because you know it's *your* fault."

"What is my fault?"

"That Hannah is dead."

His face paled, and she knew she'd really stepped over

the line—but she no longer cared. Maybe it was time to say the hard things. Just get it out there.

"What do you mean it's my fault that Hannah is dead?" he asked in a quiet tone.

"You got her that car! That stupid old VW Beetle."

"She begged for that car. You know how she loved vintage things. And she worked to earn part of it and then Mother helped her—"

"But you *knew* it wasn't safe. Bart told you those old models were dangerous. But did you listen to your own brother? No, you just went ahead and—"

"We made that car as safe as we could, Moira. Hannah only used it to go to school and town—"

"It was like giving her a loaded gun, and you know it! She was a teenager—she should've had a safe car. But you gave her a deathtrap!"

Alex looked like he'd been slapped as he turned to go into his closet. But Moira didn't care. It was time people started owning up to their responsibilities. It wasn't completely Alex's fault that Hannah died in her car…but it was partly his fault. It was time for him to own up to it. As she went to her bathroom in search of her Xanax bottle, she was glad she'd spoken her piece. She washed down another pill with lukewarm water, telling herself she'd done Alex a favor. He needed to hear the truth. Perhaps it would set him free.

Eight

AS MUCH AS I WANT TO HOLE UP IN THE TREE house all night in the hopes that my parents might be worried and concerned for my welfare, I'm pretty sure no one cares. Dad knows I'm up here and, besides a couple of texts asking me to come into the house, he's made no effort to come outside to talk to me. I know because I've kept the window open just in case he calls out or wants me to let down the ladder. He obviously has better things to do.

Meanwhile, I'm subjected to the laughter, music, and generally annoying party noises from across the street. The Baxters are in high spirits tonight. I tell myself it's because they can't wait to ship Nora off to college. The truth is I've never liked that girl. I dubbed her Nasty Nora the first time I witnessed her bullying Hannah. We'd recently moved into our house, and Hannah and I were waiting for the school bus. Nora had started by making fun of Hannah's outfit, which I thought was actually pretty nice, but when Hannah ignored her, Nora moved it up a notch by shoving my sister to the ground. Naturally, I stepped in and explicitly told Nora just what I thought of her. I'm surprised she didn't flatten me too, but maybe our mothers were watching.

Nora and Hannah were in sixth grade at the time. Looking back, I'm sure Nora was simply jealous of my pretty sister. To Nora's credit, she eventually grew out of her bullying ways. Although she's never been exactly *nice*. And even though Hannah forgave her, I didn't. Never mind that I became a bully to Hannah in later years… torturing my pretty sibling in my own sinister ways. That was different.

After it's been dark for a while, I notice an itchiness on my left ankle. I scratch it to discover a hard, hot lump, which upon closer inspection with my flashlight appears to be a bug bite. It's red and swollen and throbbing. And I'm suddenly reminded of the stories I used to tell Maddie about poisonous spiders and how they lurk in dark, shadowy, woodsy places like this very tree house.

So despite my resolution to become a backyard recluse, I wonder if perhaps I've been bitten by one. A *brown* recluse, to be more specific. So I figure it's time to sneak back into the house. If I'm about to get sick or die, I'd prefer to do it in the comfort of my own bed. Besides that, I'm feeling bad about Maddie now. Realizing what a useless sister I was to Hannah, I feel a greater responsibility to connect with Maddie. Especially considering that she'll be leaving with Grandma early in the morning. I can at least tell her good-bye and reassure her that, despite my abrupt exit from the restaurant, I didn't go jump in front of a train or anything. And knowing how she reads late into the night, I doubt she's asleep yet.

I dig around my backpack for my house key just in case my mom has locked me out, which I wouldn't put past her. To my relief the key is still there, and I'm surprised to discover the backdoor is unlocked, which is very un-mom-like. I quietly let myself inside only to discover the house is dark and silent, like they've all gone to bed. So much for fretting over my welfare. I could perish from my poisonous spider bite and they probably wouldn't find my rotting body for a week or more.

I tiptoe up the stairs, slip my backpack into my room, and then creep down the hallway to Maddie's door. I'm about to tap quietly on it, but a sound coming from in there stops me. Maddie is crying—and the sounds of her quiet sobs tear through me like a rusty knife. I hate that my baby sister is caught in the middle of our mess. Of every family member, she seems the most blameless...the most vulnerable.

"Maddie," I whisper as I crack open her door.

"Kiera?" She looks up from the book that's open in front of her, and for a moment I hope that she's crying over a sad story. But then she tosses her book aside, leaps from the bed, and rushes over to hug me. "Are you okay?"

"Yes," I assure her. "I've just been chilling in the tree house." I show her my swollen ankle. "And then I got bit and decided to come—"

"Oh, no!" Her eyes widen in horror. "Was it poisonous?"

"Maybe." I shrug it off.

She runs over to her backpack by the door. "I'll get my EpiPen!"

"No, no," I say firmly. "Thanks anyway, but I don't think that's necessary."

"How about a Benadryl?" Now she pulls out a bottle, shaking a bright pink pill into her hand and holding it out to me hopefully.

"Okay." I pop it into my mouth, swallowing it dry. "But why are you crying, Maddie?" I sit on the edge of her bed.

"Oh, I don't know." She reaches for a tissue, using it to blot her tears as she sits beside me. "I just get sad sometimes."

"About Hannah?"

"Yeah…Hannah…and our family too." She turns to look at me with watery gray eyes. "I feel like we're falling apart."

I just nod.

"Mom said such mean stuff to you tonight, Kiera. I hate that. And then Mom and Dad started to fight after you left. And Grandma tried to make it better. But it was so miserable. It's like we're not even a family anymore."

"I know." I can't think of anything comforting to say.

"Do you think it'll ever get better?"

I slip my arm around her shoulders, giving her a sideways hug. "I honestly don't know," I confess. "But I will always be your sister, Maddie. And I will always love you."

"Really?" She looks surprised.

"Really," I assure her. "I'm sorry if I haven't been there for you. I probably assumed you were okay. I mean, you're always reading a book and you usually seem like you have it pretty much together. A lot more than the rest of us."

"I just wish *Dr. Who* would take me back in time," she says wistfully.

I can't help but smile at this—her love of this British TV show. "I wish he could take me too," I admit.

"I want it to be how it used to be. I mean, we were never a perfect family, but we were a whole lot better than this. Don't you think?"

"Yes." But I consider it. "Although we probably had more problems than you realized. I mean, because of your age, you might not have noticed everything. I probably didn't either. But I do agree, if I could turn back the clock I definitely would. In a heartbeat."

She points to my hair. "But you'd keep your hair like

that, wouldn't you? Because I really like it. It's fun and different. It suits you."

I almost laugh at this.

"And you're really okay?" she asks again. "You're not just saying that?"

"I guess it depends on how you define *okay*." I sigh. "But don't worry, I would never do anything drastic, like do myself in." I point to my throbbing ankle like it's proof. "I really don't enjoy pain."

She looks relieved but then frowns. "Mom and Dad got into a bad fight after we got home."

"Really?"

She nods somberly. "Didn't you hear Dad leave?"

"He left?" Now I remember how you can't see the driveway from the tree house.

"Yeah. About an hour ago. I figured you knew. I know he was texting you at the restaurant. I think that was what they were fighting about."

I have mixed feelings about this. On one hand, it's nice to know someone cares enough about me to fight over it. On the other hand, I don't want to be blamed for their marital troubles. I can just imagine Mom's take on this. But seeing Maddie's worried expression reminds me I'm trying to reassure her. "Well, don't worry. It's not the first time Dad's left during a fight. He always comes back. Usually before anyone—besides Mom—realizes he's left. It'll be okay."

"Do you think Grandma knows?"

"Well, the guest room's not that far from Mom and Dad's room."

"I can tell she was getting stressed too." She purses her lips as if trying to decide whether to say something. "Can I tell you a secret?"

"Of course."

"And you won't tell anyone?"

"You can trust me."

"Well, last time I was at Grandma's house, you know during spring break, I overheard her talking to Uncle Bart." She lets out a sad little sigh.

"And?"

"Grandma blames herself for Hannah's accident."

"You're kidding?" I'm incredulous. "How can it possibly be her fault?"

"Because she gave Dad a thousand dollars—in secret— for Hannah's car. It was supposed to be for Hannah's seventeenth birthday, but Grandma didn't want anyone to know because she wasn't sure she could afford to do the same for you and me, you know, when we turned seventeen. Grandma told Uncle Bart that if she hadn't done that, Hannah wouldn't have gotten the old VW bug. Because otherwise Dad was going to finance a new car for her. A safer car."

I try to wrap my head around this. Besides reaffirming that Hannah was Grandma's favorite, it seems like a big leap for our grandmother to take. "Well, I think that's ridiculous."

"Really?" Maddie looks slightly hopeful.

"Grandma can't blame herself for Hannah's death. Not any more than any of us can." Of course, even as I say this I don't believe it. I know for a fact that I'm the most to blame. Try as I might to deny or block it, deep down I know the truth. I blame myself above everyone else for my sister's death. And my mom does too. But Maddie doesn't need to know about all of this. That's too much for a twelve-year-old to bear. "Well, you should try to help Grandma to see that it's *not* her fault."

"How?"

"I don't know. Maybe just by being there for her. I know she tries to act all cheerful and stuff—while the rest of us are falling apart—but underneath all that I know she's hurting too." I hug Maddie again. "It's really sweet that you'll be with her this summer. I think that alone will help a lot." Now I do something uncharacteristic—for me—I kiss my sister on the cheek. "And I hope you have a really good summer—just being a kid with Kendall. That'll probably help Grandma too—to see you two just being happy and having fun." I feel a small wave of longing, wishing I could be a little kid again too.

"And you'll be okay here by yourself…with Mom and Dad?"

I avoid her eyes and slowly nod. "Yes, I'm guessing we'll all be much better by the time you come home in August. Probably almost back to normal." Okay, this is a flat-out lie, but I don't know what else to say.

"I sure hope so." She looks down, fiddling with the buttons on her worn and nearly outgrown *Hello Kitty* pajamas that Hannah gave her for Christmas a couple years ago. "I've prayed for everyone to get better. But I think my prayers are getting ignored, because it just seems to get worse. I was actually starting to wonder if God is even real. I know Hannah believed in God...but look where that got her." She grimly shakes her head. "Hannah wanted me to believe in God too. She talked to me about it a lot last year. She gave me my first grownup kind of Bible for Christmas, right before she died. And because she's, well, not here, I wanted to keep going to church and youth group and stuff for her...but to tell you the truth, I'm not so sure about religion now. I don't really want to go to church anymore. Not by myself anyway."

Even though I can offer no encouragement about anything related to God, it makes me sad to see Maddie questioning everything like this. "Well, maybe you'll get things figured out this summer," I say lightly. "And, whether you like it or not, you can be sure Grandma will take you to church with her." I point to the clock by her bed. "In fact, you have to get up pretty early tomorrow to make it to her church on time."

"Don't remind me."

I hug her again. "Everything's going to be okay." I wonder what right I have to promise her something that I know is impossible, and yet I don't know what else to say.

"Thanks, Kiera." Her voice sounds a little brighter now. "I'm going to miss you."

"Just text me," I tell her. "Or call if you need to." And now I do something I've never ever done before, although I'd seen Hannah do it before. I tuck my little sister into bed and, for the second time tonight—and in years—I kiss her on the cheek. "Good night, Maddie, don't let the bed bugs bite."

"You should talk about bites." Her eyes twinkle then grow serious. "I hope your bite's not poisonous, Kiera, but if you need my EpiPen, it's in the outside zipper pocket on by backpack. Just come and get it if you need it."

I thank her and turn off her light. As I quietly go to my room, I feel guilty for giving her false hope just now. How dare I assure her that everything will get better when I know for a fact it won't? But how could I tell her the cold hard truth? She doesn't deserve to spend her whole summer under a black cloud of hopelessness. Autumn and reality will arrive soon enough.

Nine

MOIRA'S HEAD WAS THROBBING BY THE time she dragged herself out of bed on Sunday morning. To her dismay it was nearly eleven! Sleeping in like this was inexcusable. Something she'd chasten her daughters for doing. Or she used to... before everything changed last winter. Even so, Moira rarely slept in herself. It was lazy and unhealthy and just plain slovenly. Something Kiera would do. For all Moira knew, Kiera was still sleeping in the tree house. Well, fine, let her. The less she interacted with Moira today, the better. For everyone.

As she brushed the scum from her teeth, she knew she'd missed her opportunity to tell Maddie and Virginia good-bye this morning. That was not good, but she would call Virginia later today and apologize. And she'd text Maddie. They would both understand. Moira squinted at the haggard image in her bathroom mirror. Based on the dark smudges of eye-makeup beneath her eyes and pasty looking complexion, she knew she hadn't washed or moisturized before bed. Another careless trait that she did not admire.

She didn't actually remember going to bed. However, she did remember fighting with Alex after they got home. Vaguely. As she recalled, he'd yelled a lot. He'd been extremely angry and unreasonable. And judging by his untouched side of the bed, he'd slept somewhere else. Probably the sectional down in the basement rec room. Well, fine. Hopefully he'd wake up with a sore back.

When she finally made it into the kitchen, she saw the note Virginia had left, thanking them for their hospitality, which almost made Moira laugh, and saying that she and Maddie would grab some breakfast on the road. Well, that was probably for the best too. Moira wouldn't have been ready for Virginia's disapproval over her performance last night at dinner. She had no doubts that her mother-in-law was disappointed in her. Probably with all of them. But surely Virginia would understand what a sad night it was—being reminded of how Hannah wasn't there to graduate with her class. How much was a mother supposed to bear?

As she made a strong pot of coffee, she was resolved to do better. In fact, she decided yesterday must've been her rock bottom. Not long ago, her counselor had told her that very low day would eventually come—the moment in time when Moira felt so miserable and downhearted that the only way to look would be up. Surely, that's what yesterday had been. And, in fairness, Hannah's graduation day was quite a milestone to get beyond. And now they had done it.

But as she filled a mug with coffee, Moira remembered that Hannah's eighteenth birthday was in August. How would she get past *that?* When would it get better? Probably never. Hearing a noise upstairs, she figured it must be Kiera. The tree house probably hadn't been too comfortable. But it would've served her right to have been locked out. Wasn't that one of the things she and Alex had argued about last night? Moira had wanted to lock the door and he'd said no. Stubborn man.

As Moira sat down at the breakfast bar, she felt another small prick of guilt. Perhaps she had been too hard on Kiera at dinner. Maybe she should attempt to make amends. But didn't Kiera owe her an apology too? What about the things she'd said and done yesterday? Whatever happened to kids respecting their parents? Had she allowed Kiera to get away with too much these last few months? Moira wasn't stupid, she knew that she could never mold Kiera into another Hannah. But wasn't it Moira's job, as a mother, to ensure that Kiera grew up into the best person she could possibly be? But how?

More and more, Moira felt like she was losing her grasp on…well, everything. Her duties as a wife and mom used to come so naturally to her, so much so that she'd been aware of how others put her on a pedestal of sorts. And she hadn't particularly minded. Especially considering the way she'd been raised. Moira's mother had been a hot mess. But Moira's children's teachers had always known that if there was a need for last minute Valentine cupcakes or an extra mom on a field trip, Moira was the one to call. Or if Alex needed to bring a last-minute client home for dinner, he'd always expected that Moira could pull something together. But not since January.

Besides barely cooking anymore, Moira knew she was barely pulling her weight at the realty agency as well. Oh, sure, Lisa had been patient with her, even suggesting that Moira take a year-long sabbatical to recover from her grief, but Moira had insisted on continuing to work. Partly because she had a number of good listings and partly because she'd hoped it would distract her. But she'd only made one sale since January. The rest had been just mindless wheel spinning. Like yesterday.

She stared at the calendar hanging on the fridge—this was still early June and buying season had barely begun. It was too soon to throw in the towel. If there were just some way to get past this, some magic pill that would make her feel better, help her to function. Not like what she'd done last night. Clearly, that had been a mistake. And yet it had provided an escape too. And considering everything, escaping still seemed a tempting option. Who needed this much pain?

At the sound of shuffling feet, she looked over to see

that Kiera was just coming into the kitchen. Weighing her words and controlling the urge to say something sarcastic, Moira decided to wait. Let Kiera figure this one out.

"Oh!" Kiera jumped to see her mother at the breakfast bar. "You're up?"

"Of course, I'm up," she snapped. "Looks like you just crawled out though."

"I've been up for a few hours." Kiera filled a coffee mug.

"You drink coffee now?" Moira frowned disapproval.

"I've been drinking coffee for months." Kiera got out the milk, adding a little and giving it a swirl before taking a sip. "That a problem?" She narrowed her eyes slightly as she replaced the milk carton.

"Well, if you don't care about having your growth stunted." Moira knew that was a silly thing to say, but it was too late.

"That's an old wives' tale." Kiera watched Moira over the rim of her coffee mug. "And I'm as tall as I'm going to get anyway. I'm sixteen, in case you've forgotten."

"Whatever."

Kiera lowered her mug and, to Moira's surprised, it seemed like her expression softened. "Are you okay?" she asked with what almost sounded like concern.

"Do you even care?" Again, Moira regretted her words. What was wrong with her?

Kiera shrugged and started to turn away.

"Look," Moira said quickly. "I'm not proud of how I acted last night."

Kiera turned back to look at her, waiting.

"I know that you got your feelings hurt. Your father made that perfectly clear." Moira scowled. "But my feelings were hurt too, Kiera. You can be pretty difficult. And I was already upset about the whole graduation thing. A little compassion goes a long way, you know?" She looked intently at her rebellious daughter.

"I know." Kiera returned her gaze. "It's a *two-way* street, Mom."

"See!" Moira pointed at her. "There you go—attacking me again! Like you think I don't have any feelings!"

"I *know* you have feelings!" Kiera used a word that would've cost a quarter in the quarter jar—except that no one kept track anymore. "But so do I! And so does Dad and Maddie! You're not the only one who's hurting in this family!"

Moira had no response to that. Of course, she knew they were all hurting. Had no doubts about that. But she suspected if there were a way to weigh and measure guilt, she would prove to all of them that she carried the bulk of it. "Look, Kiera. I'm not doing a good job of this, but I know I owe you an apology. But I believe you owe me one too." Moira folded her arms across her front, waiting.

Kiera looked doubtful.

"So?" Moira pursed her lips. "I'm waiting."

"So?" Kiera's forehead creased. "You mean that was

it? *That* was your apology? Well, fine then. I guess maybe
I owe you an apology too. What I need to apologize for is
a total mystery to me. But, hey, whatever." She shrugged
and turned away.

"Wait!"

Kiera paused without turning around.

"I'm sorry I hurt your feelings last night," Moira said
quickly. "I'm sorry I said mean things."

Kiera slowly turned around with arched brows. "Really?"

"Yes. Really. I know it was wrong. And it's not how
I want to act. But sometimes…well, it's like I can't help
myself. I want to do one thing and I do the complete opposite. It's like my brain has been rewired." And now, despite her resolve not to, Moira began to cry.

"Well, okay, I get that. And I'm sorry too, Mom." Kiera's voice grew gentler. "Maybe we can get better at this."

Moira reached for a paper napkin, blotting her eyes
with it. "I hope so."

"Grandma and Maddie said to tell you good-bye."

Moira felt a fresh wave of guilt. "You were up that early?"

"Yeah. I wanted to say good-bye."

Moira angrily wadded the napkin. Was Kiera just trying to make her feel worse? "Well, that was nice of you,"
she said in a chilly tone. "Was your father up too?"

"Dad wasn't here."

Moira considered this. "Did you see him leave? Did he get up for an early game of golf?"

"He left last night."

"Last night?" Moira felt her chest tighten. "And never came back?"

Kiera shook her head.

"How do you know? I mean did you see him leave? Are you sure he's not back? Maybe in the basement or—"

"He's not here, Mom. Maddie saw him leave last night. His car was still gone this morning."

"Oh...." Moira's hand trembled as she picked up the coffee mug. What exactly *had* she said to Alex last night? She vaguely remembered suggesting that he should leave. Had he really thought she'd meant it? *Had* she meant it?

"Do you know where he went?" Kiera asked quietly.

"Of course, not! How would *I* know?" Moira demanded.

"Sorry—I just wonder—"

"Well, don't worry about it," she snapped. "He'll be back." And then she turned and hurried back to her room. Locking the door, she headed straight for the medicine cabinet. Perhaps she'd been wrong—perhaps she hadn't hit her real rock bottom yet. But she had a feeling a hard landing was in her future. In the meantime, she needed something to take the edge off...just to get her through this.

Ten

AS I FIX MYSELF A LATE LUNCH, I FEEL TO-tally fed up. With everyone and everything! Swearing under my breath, I stomp around the kitchen, slamming doors closed, and clattering about noisily. What do I care if I disturb Mom? She deserves to be disturbed! Seriously, does she plan to sleep all day?

I've barely sat down to eat my peanut butter and jam sandwich when Mom shuffles into the kitchen. Her hair is still messy and she's got a hard to read expression—a cross between a scowl and bewilderment, but when she begins to speak, her speech sounds slow and slurred. "What're you doing out here?" she asks, leaning onto the breakfast bar. "Makin' all that noise?"

"Fixing lunch." I peer curiously at her. "What's wrong with you?"

"Nothin's wrong with me." She steps back, a bit unsteadily.

"You're high, aren't you?" I stand now, going over to look closely at Mom's face. "What kind of pills are you taking, anyway?"

"None of your business."

"That's just perfect," I say with sarcasm. "Dad's left and you're turning into a drug addict again. Just perfect."

"I am *not* an *addict!*" Mom's eyes flash in anger, and I jump in surprise as she loudly slaps her hand on the countertop. "I am your *mother!* And I expect some respect, young lady!"

"Whatever." I gather my sandwich and glass of milk and, not wanting to prolong this confrontation, exit the kitchen. But instead of going up to my room, I march straight out the front door. Maybe it will give Mom something to think about. Then, making sure that Mom's not watching, I hurry across the yard to the tree house, let down the ladder, and, balancing my lunch in one hand, climb up.

It figures that the tree house is hot and stuffy today. I heard the temp is supposed to near triple digits. So I open the window, not that it helps much. Remembering the still-swollen bite on my ankle, I perform a quick search for spiders. Satisfied that none are lurking about, I sit down and finish my lunch. Then, despite the sweltering heat, I pull out Hannah's diary and start to read. The entries continue to sound dark and depressed. Completely un-Hannah-like. Except that I can tell that she was really hurting.

It's frustrating and painful to read how low she got, and how long she let it eat away at her, all the while using her cheerful face to hide it from everyone. It especially hurts to think that if she had trusted me enough, she could've confided in me—I know I would've understood—and yet she didn't. And that was my fault. Instead, she let her whole life get ruined. All because of that horrible night with Maxwell the jerk. I hate him!

As unsettling as it is to read about Hannah's unbearable sadness, it's also weirdly comforting. Comfort laced with guilt, anyway. But somehow it makes me feel better to know that my perfect sister had problems too. Like I can finally relate to her. Now that it's too late. But, honestly, if Hannah were alive, I actually believe we could've gotten closer because of this.

And yet, as far as I can see, Hannah never told anyone about her suffering. I suppose I get that too, because I tend to keep things inside. Yet Hannah's reasons were different than mine. She kept her pain inside to please others—because no one expected Hannah Josephson to be anything besides sweetness and light. Meanwhile, I keep my stuff hidden deep just because that's how I am—I don't like wearing my heart on my sleeve. I don't want anyone's pity. But where Hannah concealed her pain with a sweet smile, I hide mine with a sour snarl.

I pause from reading—it's so hot I am actually sweating. Could I be on the verge of heat stroke? Maybe I don't care. That's because the next entry is too compelling to put this book down. It feels like Hannah is on the verge of something—and I need to find out what. And so, despite the heat, I read on.

I wish I didn't love my family so much. It would be a lot easier to make my exit if I hated them. Because that's what I've decided to do. Just bow out. Escape the pain that has become my life. It's been two months now, and I honestly don't know how else to live with all this sadness. It just seems to get worse with each day. I've managed to alienate my real friends. And thanks to (name I refuse to write or speak) my reputation is ruined. If I didn't care about my family, if I didn't love them, it would be very simple to end this. And I have it all figured out too. I've heard it's the way our military men have been taking their own lives. But thinking about my family…well, it gives me pause. I know my parents would be devastated. So would Maddie. And even though Kiera pretends to hate me, I suspect she would be hurt too. It's for their sake that I'm hanging on, but—

The sound of someone yelling down below the tree house jerks me back into the present. I can tell it's Mom, and she sounds upset. So much so that I instantly get worried that something horrible might have happened to Maddie…or Dad.

"What is it?" I yell out the window.

"Get down here," she insists. "I need to talk to you. Now!"

I stuff the diary back beneath the loose board and quickly scale down the ladder, not even bothering to pull the rope that puts the ladder back into the tree house. "What's wrong?" I use the back of my hand to wipe the sweat from my brow.

"What're you doing up there?" she demands.

"Getting away from you," I spout back.

"Why is your face so red? Why are you sweating?"

"Because it's stinking hot up there." I plant my hands on my hips. "What do you want, anyway? Why are you so upset? Is it Maddie? Or Dad?"

"Come in the house." She spins away. "I'll tell you in there."

Still worried there might be another family tragedy, I mutely follow her into the cool dark house.

"What's going on?" I persist as I follow her into the living room.

"It's your dad." Mom flops down on the couch.

"What's wrong?" I demand. "Is he hurt?"

"No, no…." She waves a dismissive hand.

"Well, what then?" I sink into a chair across from her.

"I want you to contact him."

"What? *Why*?"

"Because he won't speak to me."

I shrug. What a surprise.

She narrows her eyes. "And I'm worried about him."

"Worried?" I study her closely, suspecting that she is just playing me now.

"He left his cholesterol medicine here." She glances away. "I'm worried he might need it. And it's a Sunday. What if he can't fill a prescription?"

Okay, this does make a little sense. Still…I'm not sure.

"I want you to get in touch with him, Kiera. He'll answer your call. Or you can text him. Whatever. I just want you to make sure he's okay—okay?"

"That's all?" I stand. Maybe she's not being as manipulative as I assumed.

"Well…." She stands too. "You could tell him that I'm not well, Kiera. Tell him that I'm upset and that I'm worried about him…and that I need him to come home."

"Those are things you should tell him yourself," I point out.

"But he's ignoring my calls."

"I'm sure he has his reasons." I slowly back out of the living room, hoping for a smooth getaway.

"I want him to know that I'm suffering, Kiera. Can't you just tell him that much for me?"

I shrug, taking another step backward. "I'll text him for you… and let him know he should get his cholesterol medicine. But I can't promise more than—"

"Kiera!" Her voice is laced with anger. "I ask you to do one simple thing and—"

"I am not going to get in the middle of your spat with Dad," I declare with equal emotion. "Don't even ask me—"

"You are a worthless daughter!" she spews. "Totally useless." And now she crumbles into tears. I know she wants me to feel guilty, and I refuse to fall for it. While her head is down I make a run for my room.

And yet as I remove my phone from the charger, I *do* feel guilty. I even imagine what Hannah would do. Of course, she would totally cave to Mom. She always did. That was just one of the many reasons they got along so well. But that is not me. As Mom plainly tells me all the time, I am not my sister. Still, as I text a brief message to Dad, I do wonder… What would it hurt for me to show more compassion to my mom? Sure, it would be a compromise for me. But for all I know it might actually improve our relationship. It could even make my life easier. Wouldn't that be worth something? And yet I know I can't do this. How can I give to her what she refuses to give to me? Maybe someday my mom will show me some compassion, and then I'll do the same. Yeah, right…like that'll happen.

I jump when I hear my phone ringing. And to my pleasant surprise it's Dad. "Hello?" I say eagerly. "Are you okay?"

"Sure, I'm okay, honey. I didn't mean to worry you."

"Maddie said you left last night. After you and Mom fought."

"Oh, great. She heard all that?"

"Unfortunately. But I reassured her that everything would be okay."

"You did?" He sounds grateful.

"Yeah, and she seemed fine this morning. I told her and Grandma good-bye for you. Grandma assumed you were playing golf, and I just let her think so."

"Thanks, Kiera. You're a good girl."

I mutter a quiet "Thanks" but cannot even describe how nice it feels for him to say that about me. "Anyway, Mom's worried that you need your cholesterol medicine."

"Yeah, I probably do." He lets out a sigh. "But I'm not ready to come home."

"Where are you, Dad?"

"I'm at the office."

"Did you spend the night there?"

"Uh-huh." He makes a quiet groan. "Keep that between you and me and the lamppost, honey. I'd be in hot water if anyone found out about it."

"So are you coming home tonight?"

"I, uh, I don't think so."

"Hey, how about I ride my bike to town and bring your prescription to you?" I offer hopefully. Suddenly it feels very important to see Dad. In person.

"You'd do that for me?"

"Yeah, of course."

"I could meet you halfway. How about Ferris Park?"

"Sure." I glance at my clock. "I can be there by four."

"Great. Maybe we can grab a hotdog...and talk some more."

I'm so excited about getting some time like this with Dad that I actually change my t-shirt and brush my teeth. Pretty minimal, I know. But for me it's a definite improvement. Then, as I go downstairs, I prepare myself for Mom. Somehow I need to get Dad's prescription from her without an inquisition. To my relief, I can hear her talking to someone on the phone in the kitchen about a real estate listing. And, knowing she'll be furious if she finds out, I sneak down the hall to my parents' bedroom and straight for the medicine cabinet. Of course, this is not as simple as I'd hoped. They have a lot of prescriptions. Mostly for Mom. And mostly from her shrink. I'm tempted to pocket these as well, but I know she'd have my hide if I did. Instead, I take two bottles with Dad's name on them. Hopefully one of them is for cholesterol.

As I pedal toward the park, I feel like I'm on the cusp of something big. I can't even wrap my head around it, whether it's big-good or big-bad, but I feel like some kind of change is in the air. I'm relieved to see that Dad is already there. Sitting on a park bench and looking rather sad and dejected. He's got on the same clothes as last night, but they look uncharacteristically rumpled for him. And as I get closer, I can see he hasn't shaved. He jumps to his feet when he sees me and suddenly we're embracing like we haven't seen each other in months. And to my embarrassment I begin to cry.

"Oh, Kiera." He frowns to see my tears. "What is it?"

I shrug, using my hand to wipe my face. "Just feeling emotional."

"Because of your mom and me?"

"Because of everything." I remember reading Hannah's words about how much she loved our family. What would she think of us now?

"The Josephsons have really been through the wringer this year." He leads me over to his park bench.

I just nod as I sit down.

"I keep thinking it can't get worse." He sighs as he sits. "And then it does."

"I know."

"Kiera, I'm so sorry for how your mom treated you last night. I realized too late that I should've intervened for you, but I honestly thought that keeping quiet was going to preserve the peace. I was wrong." He looks into my eyes. "I'm sorry. And I hope you'll forgive me."

"Of course. But it wasn't your fault. And FYI, I'm pretty sure that Mom was high last night. Not just on wine either."

His smile is sad. "You got that right."

"She wanted me to tell you how bad she's feeling today."

He looks slightly hopeful now. "Did she apologize?"

I shrug. "I don't know…sort of. Maybe you could call it that."

"Well, I hope she *is* sorry. Even so…I'm not ready to go home yet."

"Where will you stay?" I study him. "Not in your office."

He shakes his head and removes his phone from his shirt pocket. "I'm waiting for a call from Larry. His wife and kids are up in Canada. He's got the house to himself while they visit her family for about a month. I thought maybe I could bach it with him while they're gone."

"Oh?" For some reason this really concerns me. Like Dad is abandoning us completely. Like a captain jumping a sinking ship while his crew is still aboard. I feel the tears coming again. "Do you really think that's a good idea?"

"I just need some time to clear my head, honey."

"But a whole month?"

"I might not need that much time. But a few days, maybe a week…for starters."

"What will Mom say?"

He slowly shakes his head. "She's the one who told me to leave last night."

"Oh?"

"You could come visit me there, Kiera. I'm sure Larry wouldn't mind."

The idea of visiting Dad and Larry at their bachelor pad feels awkward, but I simply nod, picking at the frayed strings of my cutoffs.

"I know this is hard on you, honey. But it's something your mom and I need to figure out. I thought by now we'd have moved forward a little. But your mom just seems stuck in the past. Like she can't move on. And I understand. But we *all* miss Hannah. And being miserable won't bring her back."

"And it wouldn't make Hannah happy." I remember what I read earlier today. How Hannah wanted to kill herself, but was reluctant because she knew how it would hurt us. And yet…she's gone anyway and we *are* hurting.

"I've told your mom that very thing. Hannah would hate seeing us falling apart like this, six months later." He balls his fists. "But your mom can't hear it. And besides…" He purses his lips.

"Besides what?" I ask.

"Oh, you know. Mom blames me for Hannah's death."

"Because of the car business?"

"Yeah." He grimly shakes his head. "Hannah wanted that old VW so badly."

"I remember."

"Your mom thought it was a bad idea. It was almost like she knew, like women's intuition… I'd give anything to have listened to her."

"But remember what the police said?" I remind him. "Not very many cars could survive a wreck like that."

"Maybe not. But I guess we'll never know."

"Well, you're not the only one Mom blames," I say quietly. This is a subject I usually try to avoid. But since Dad's already gone there...well, it seems only fair.

"That's just the problem, Kiera. Everyone needs to stop blaming everyone. It's killing all of us. It has to end. And that's exactly what I told your mom last night. Not that she was listening." He closes his eyes with a long, deflated sigh. "Maybe if I spend some time away...maybe I'll get her attention. Maybe she'll listen."

And if she doesn't? I can't vocalize the questions racing through my mind now. What if Mom and Dad never work things out? What if this "time away" turns into something more permanent? Like a legal separation? Then a divorce? What happens to us then? What about Maddie and me? Where do we fit into this mess?

Eleven

I'M NOT FEELING VERY HOPEFUL AS I WAIT for my interview with my grandma's friend. The waiting room seems cold and sterile, and the receptionist doesn't even smile when I tell her I have an appointment. As I observe a man in a suit enter an office, I'm aware that my jeans and t-shirt, which are clean but well-worn, are completely inappropriate for a job interview. At least I didn't wear the flip-flops my mom detests. Because I rode my bike, I'm wearing my black Chuck Taylors, which, like the rest of my ensemble, are a bit frayed around the edges. But it's not like I wanted to work here in the first place. Feeling like a fish out of water, I'm about to sneak out and go home when I hear the receptionist call out my name.

"Ms. Peterson will see you now," she tells me with a blank expression.

I thank her then go to the door she's indicated and timidly stick in my head. "Hello?"

"Come in, come in," an older woman says warmly. I think she's my grandma's age, but she seems younger somehow. Maybe it's her tie-dyed shirt that gives this impression. And her hair, which is brown streaked with gray, is pulled back in a ponytail. "You must be Kiera Josephson." As she stands to grasp my hand, I see that, like me, she's wearing blue jeans. Only hers are the kind the older folks wear. "Virginia told me a bit about you, but I'd like to hear more." She nods to the chair. "Please, sit down."

As I sit, I notice a framed vintage poster behind her. It's for a Rolling Stones concert, circa 1969. "That's cool." I point to the poster.

She chuckles. "Helps to prove what some people already assume, that I'm just an old hippie."

"Are you?" I ask then wish I hadn't.

But she just laughs. "Well, I've tried to hold onto the good parts of hippie-hood and set the others aside." She points to me. "Now tell me more about yourself, Kiera. I know you lost your older sister last winter. I'm sorry about that."

Although I've heard those same words more times than I care to number these last six months, something about the way she says this sort of unglues me. Or maybe it's just all the crud my family's been through lately. Or reading my sister's diary. But to my embarrassment and dismay, I begin to tear up. "I, uh, I'm sorry about this." I accept the box of tissues she's passing to me. "I'm usually pretty tough." I wipe my eyes and nose. "Some people think I'm too tough." I take in a breath and sit up straighter. "But it's been kind of a rough year."

"I know. Virginia said as much. She also told me that you have a kind heart and that you're very good with younger children. Apparently she's observed you with your little sister and your cousin."

"I usually end up being the baby-sitter when we're at her house." I shrug. "But I don't mind. Maddie and Kendall are pretty easy to manage."

"But your grandmother seems to think you're good at it. That you have empathy for younger kids. Do you think that's true?"

I consider this. "I guess so. I remember how I felt as a kid. I wanted people to treat me with respect. Not like I was a dumb kid and second-class citizen. I guess I try to treat kids the way I wanted to be treated."

She nods. "I like that." Now she asks me about my hobbies and interests and I tell her that I used to be into sports, but the last few years have been more about art and music. Although I don't admit that I've pretty much ignored my guitar these past six months, or that all the sketches in my sketchpad are so dark and creepy that I'd be embarrassed for anyone to see it. I honestly don't know what I do with my spare time anymore.

"Virginia told me you're quite talented on guitar, and a very fine artist too."

I shrug. "What else can she say? She's my grandmother." Still, it feels nice to think Grandma noticed these things. Maybe I've been wrong about her.

"Well, I have a feeling you could be a good fit for us, Kiera." She leans forward, peering closely at me, and I wonder if she's about to offer me a job—and how do I feel about it? "You see, we're implementing a new program." She twirls a pencil between her fingers. "Actually, it's an old program, but I'm trying to bring it back. This summer is kind of experimental. A trial of sorts. But I'm betting my job that it works."

"Meaning you'll be fired if it doesn't?"

She barely smiles. "Something like that." She waves a hand. "But my friends all think I should be retired by now anyway. Anyway, here's the deal, Kiera, we're hiring young people like yourself to work as park counselors."

"What does a park counselor do?" I imagine myself on a park bench asking a tree about its troubles. Does it harbor ill feelings toward its mother…?

"A park counselor is on hand to supervise kids' activities at the park. You would help to manage the free lunch program, teach arts and crafts, and organize games and activities. Help to keep the kids occupied and out of trouble."

"Kind of like a baby-sitter?" I try not to look overly disappointed.

"Not exactly. More like providing a community service to children who could use a good role model."

"Role model?" I feel my stomach turn. "I, uh, I don't really think—"

"According to Virginia, you've been an honor student and—"

"My grades slipped some this past year."

"You've had a hard year, Kiera. I think it's understandable."

"Yeah, but...." I run my fingers through my chopped hair. "I'm not sure parents would see me as a very good role model." I can just imagine someone like my mom questioning a person like me working as a park counselor. I try to think of a good excuse to thank her and leave.

"I have a specific park in mind for you. Are you familiar with Greenwood Park?"

"Not exactly, but I know about the Greenwood area."

"Then you probably know it's a low-income neighborhood. Some of the kids are a bit neglected around there. As a result, the park can turn into a magnet for problems. I need a tough, no-nonsense counselor in that park—but one with a heart."

I imagine a brawl breaking out among the young hoodlums—what would I do to stop it? "Uh, maybe you need a male counselor."

"Actually, I've already hired a college boy. But I want two counselors at this particular park. A guy *and* a girl."

I'm still uncertain, but as we continue to talk, I realize

that I really like this Ms. Peterson. I can tell that she genuinely cares about kids and seems to care about me too.

"So you're actually offering me a job?" I ask. "I mean, I haven't even filled out an application or anything."

"I've done my own research." Her pale gray eyes twinkle. "No police record. Good academic record—although you're right, your grades did drop a bit this year. But nothing that should concern you too much, Kiera. I'm sure you'll get back into the swing of things next year. And to your question, yes, I'm offering you the job. It's six hours a day. Weekdays only. Ten to four. And...you'll have to wear a uniform."

"A uniform?" I cringe to imagine myself dressed like Smokey the Bear.

She smiles. "It's so kids will recognize that you're a park employee."

"And not some creep on the prowl for kids?"

She nods. "And so they'll give you some respect." She folds her hands. "Now, if you don't want this job, I will understand. There are many other willing applicants, and I need to make a decision today. Bernard started working at Greenwood last week, and I know he can use a hand. Particularly with the little girls."

I take in a deep breath and, still uncertain and feeling concerned about the uniform, I solemnly nod. "I think it sounds like a good job, Ms. Peterson. Thank you for considering me for it. I would like to accept."

"Wonderful." She stands to shake my hand. "And you

can call me Val. All the park counselors do." She picked
up some papers. "Fill these out before you leave and give
them to the receptionist. Her name is Cynthia, and she'll
help you with a uniform."

"When do I start?"

"ASAP." She grins. "I told Bernard I might be bringing
you by today. Just to look around and get introduced. But,
if you like, you could start tomorrow. That is, if you don't
mind doing a bit of orientation today."

"Okay." I pick up the papers, wondering if I'm going
to regret this. But at the same time, I remember my mess
of a family and my hope to earn enough money to emancipate myself. "I forgot to ask about wages. I assume it's
probably minimum or thereabouts."

"It's a little better than that." She walks me to the door.
"Let me know when you're done with Cynthia, then I'll
drive you over to Greenwood to look around."

I thank her then go out to let Cynthia know I'll need
a uniform. To my surprise, she warms up now. "So Val
hired you? Just like that, huh?"

I shrug. "Yeah, but I still need to fill out these papers."

Cynthia asks me what size I wear and then heads into
a backroom. Meanwhile I sit down and, with the help of
my cell phone for phone numbers and addresses, I fill
out the paperwork. Before long, Cynthia emerges with
my uniform. To my relief, it's not too bad looking. Two
khaki colored short-sleeved shirts and a pair of shorts as
well as long pants, along with an olive green canvas belt.

"You might need to cinch in the pants and shorts," she tells me. "They're a size bigger than you asked for, but everything's cotton so it might shrink. And you'll probably want to launder them first. They're imported and have a funny smell to them."

I thank her and hand over the paperwork.

She glances over the papers. "And I'll order you a badge with your name on it." She points to blank spot on my application. "Oh, you'll need a parent's signature here."

I grimace to think of asking my mom for this, since I'm determined to ignore her as much as possible for the rest of the summer.

"I can make a copy of this page and you can get the signature and bring it back later if you like."

I glance at the clock over her desk. "My dad's office is just a couple of blocks away," I explain. "If I hurry I might catch him before he goes to lunch. Will you let Val know I'll be right back?"

She agrees and I take off, catching my dad just as he's heading for the elevator. I'm relieved to see he looks a little less rumpled than he did on Sunday, but his expression is still slightly grim. However, he smiles to see me. "Kiera," he exclaims as I meet him in the hallway. "What're you doing here?" His smile fades. "Anything wrong?"

"No, no, not at all." I wonder if the day will ever come when my family doesn't assume the worst about surprise visits or phone calls. I explain about the park counselor job and my need for a signature.

"That's fabulous, Kiera." He walks me back to his office, borrowing a pen from his receptionist to sign my form. "Congratulations, honey. Sounds like a fun summer job." As we head back to the elevator together, he takes me aside. "Kiera, can I ask a favor?"

I eagerly agree, hoping he's about to announce he's coming back home and wants me to pave the way by tipping off my mom. But it's just the opposite. Dad asks me to gather up some things for him. "I'll text you a list," he explains. "Then when your mom's not home, you just put everything in some of those yard debris trash bags and leave them near my golf clubs and junk in the garage. Then if you could let me know when your mom's not home, I'll slip by and pick it all up."

"Does this mean you'll be gone for a long time?" I ask with concern.

"I honestly don't know, Kiera. But I do feel your mom and I need some time and space between us...to figure things out. I'd come over and get the stuff while she's there except that I know it'll just stress her out. Better to do this on the lowdown."

I want to question how him staying away will help anything, but I can tell by his expression, he's not comfortable with this conversation—especially this close to his office and with his coworkers now heading for their lunch breaks. So I simply agree to do as asked and we walk to the elevator together.

"How about I take you to lunch?" he offers as we go

down. But I explain my new boss is waiting to give me my orientation.

"That's great," he says as we exit the elevator. He halts me with a hand on my arm before I can head out the door. "I want you to feel free to come see me anytime," he says quietly. "Larry said you're welcome there. And you know where he lives, don't you?"

"Yeah, sure," I tell him. "Maybe this weekend. I only work on weekdays."

"Great." Dad nods eagerly. "Maybe we can throw some steaks on the grill." He frowns. "Or some tofu or broccoli or something."

I roll my eyes. "Yeah, that sounds yummy."

"Larry's got a real nice pool that no one's using, and it's supposed to be hot this weekend. Maybe you'd like to bring a friend over and just hang out."

"I'll keep that in mind." I don't care to admit that I'm pretty much friendless these days or that I've managed to alienate almost everyone. Instead I hug him good-bye then hurry on back to the parks and rec building to give Cynthia my parent-signed application.

Before long, Val and I are in her little electric car, on our way to Greenwood Park. But I still have some concerns and reservations. Mostly about myself. What if I'm no good at this? Or the kids hate me? Or this Bernard dude is some uptight bossy type who wants to run the show? As we get nearer, I reassure myself that I can quit if necessary. But at the same time, I realize that I don't want to disappoint Val. Especially since she really seems to believe in me.

The Greenwood area is pretty rundown and sad. Small houses with peeling paint and weedy yards with junk strewn about, and beat-up vehicles parked along the street. Not the sort of real estate my mother would care to list.

"I'm sorry to say that Greenwood Park, like its neglected neighborhood, is rather derelict too." Val sighs as she pulls into a small parking lot. "But one of the plans of our new counselor program is for kids to help with some improvements. Bernard already has some ideas."

As we go through the chain-link gate, it's obvious that this park has seen better days. But for some reason this doesn't discourage me. If anything, it suddenly makes me feel like maybe this truly is the right job for me. And seeing a handful of rag-tag kids chasing a soccer ball with a tall guy gives me hope as well. It's quite possible that these kids really do need some help and supervision and encouragement. Of course, it's a little unsettling to see a cluster of young teens huddled near the rest room. They're probably just smoking, but I wonder if they could present trouble. But at least it won't be me here alone to face them.

Val calls to Bernard and, excusing himself from the soccer game, a tallish young man with dark curly hair jogs over to meet me. He's slender and looks slightly nerdish with black rimmed glasses—not to mention what looks somewhat like a Boy Scout uniform. But as Val introduces us, I get the impression he's fairly laidback and friendly.

"You like the uniform?" he says in a teasing tone. "All we need are the hats and we'll look just like Ranger Rick."

I laugh. "I remember Ranger Rick. Wasn't he a raccoon?"

We joke and visit a bit, then Val tells him that I'll start tomorrow. "And I hear that Kiera plays guitar and is a pretty good artist."

"Awesome." He nods. "I thought it might be fun to make a little campfire on a cooler day, make s'mores and sing camp songs, you know?"

"Sounds like fun."

"Why don't you give Kiera a quick tour while I take this?" Val holds up her chiming phone and steps away.

Bernard shows me around the playground, which isn't much. He points to what looks like an old shed in need of paint. "We keep the sports equipment and art supplies and stuff in there. And make sure it's always locked." He glances toward the teens by the rest room. "Just in case." He pats the side of the shed. "I thought it'd be fun to paint some kind of mural on here. Maybe you could take charge of that."

"Sure. That's a great idea."

We're just heading back to Val when soccer kids run up to Bernard, clustering and complaining that "Levi and Jordie cheated" and begging him to come back and help with the game. "Hang on a minute," he says loudly. "You need to meet Kiera. She's—"

"Your girlfriend," one of the boys teases.

"No, she's going to be a new park counselor—starting tomorrow," he clarifies.

"Are you leaving or something?" A dirty-faced boy narrows his eyes at Bernard.

"No, Will. Not at all," he assures him. "Kiera and I both will be working here. All summer long."

The kids peer curiously at me then turn back to Bernard, eagerly tugging on both his arms. "Your fans await," I tell him. "See you tomorrow."

Val insists on taking me to the food cart area downtown for some lunch. Fortunately there's a vegan cart where I can get a burrito and drink. Then we take our food back to her office, where we have a working lunch and she gives me what she calls a condensed orientation. I pay close attention and even make a few notes in the back of the handbook she gave me, but it's a lot to take in. Once again, I question myself. Am I really ready for this kind of responsibility? She keeps assuring me that Bernard and I are not legally responsible for the kids in the park. "No more than a forest ranger is responsible for people who camp in a state park," she explains. "You're there as an advisor and helper. An employee of the park district, to make the park a better place for the children. But you and Bernard are not their baby-sitters."

"And we have the right to send rule-breakers home?" I ask, remembering the smoking teens by the bathroom.

"You have the right—especially if you think a delinquent is a safety threat to anyone. But I hope you'll see beyond some of their bad behavior—and find ways to help them to engage. The purpose of this program is to improve the whole neighborhood—for everyone. Like I said, it's something of an experiment, but I really want it to work." She asks if I have any more questions.

"I don't think so." I hold up my counselor handbook. "But I'll study this at home."

"I'll be doing a full day of group orientation on Friday." She tosses her empty soda cup into the trash, and I suspect we're done. "For the other park counselors that I'm hiring this week. But Greenwood Park was my top priority. I wanted counselors in there immediately—before trouble has a chance to start."

"Do you want me to attend the Friday orientation too?" I slide my handbook into my backpack.

"I don't think it'll be necessary. I can tell you're an intelligent young woman, Kiera. And Bernard is top notch. I think you two can handle it. And, of course, if any questions arise, feel free to call or text me. And, as I've already said, if anything illegal comes up, call the police. 911 for emergencies, and the non-emergency number for anything else. Make sure that number is in your phone."

"I will," I promise.

"And I forgot to ask, Kiera—I assume you have transportation to get to work?"

"My bike." I nod. "I think Greenwood's about a fifteen-minute ride from my house. No big deal."

"Great." She stands. "I think you're going to be good for those kids, Kiera. I can tell you've got empathy—and grit. You'll need both." She shook my hand again. "Good luck."

I thank her again and, picking up my backpack where my uniform is already rolled up and neatly tucked inside, I head down to the bike rack. As I unlock my bike, I can hardly believe it—I got a job. I'm officially a parks and rec employee now. How weird is that? Part of me wants to celebrate...but the rest of me is certain I've made a huge mistake. What on earth qualifies me to be a park counselor, of all things? My own life is pretty much a mess—how can one mess help another? As I pedal home, I remind myself that it's not like I signed a binding contract. If it doesn't work out, I can always quit. And yet, I hope it does work out. I really do.

I'm not surprised that my mom isn't home. Actually, I'm relieved. I have no desire to tell my mom I got a job. She'd probably question my sanity in assuming I could handle a job like this...or else she'd make fun of me for having a job that requires a funny looking uniform. I don't need any of that right now. In fact, the less our paths cross this summer, the happier I will be. And maybe by next fall, if things don't improve around here—which seems likely—I'll have stockpiled enough money to move out and declare my independence from this madhouse.

I'm just about to head to my room when I hear my phone ping with a text message. Seeing Dad's list reminds me of my promise, and since Mom's not home, I decide to get to it. Hopefully she won't show up and catch me. I cannot imagine the fireworks show that would incur. Determined to be fast about this, I grab a box of plastic trash bags and start filling them—checking every few minutes to be sure my mom doesn't show up.

Mom still isn't home by the time I drag several large bags to the garage, stashing them by Dad's golf clubs. And our garage is cluttered enough that I doubt that Mom will even notice them. The last things on Dad's list are personal items from their bathroom that I put into a brown paper sack. Out of curiosity, I give my mom's Xanax bottle a shake and am surprised to see it's nearly empty. Good and bad. Good that she's almost out of them, bad that she's used so many. But, telling myself that her stress levels are probably high, I close the cabinet and hurry back to the garage, nestling the box behind the trash bags.

I text my dad, informing him that his garbage bags are waiting and the coast is clear. Since it's not four yet, and Mom usually doesn't come home until around five, I'm guessing it's safe for him to come by. He texts back that he's on his way, and I open the garage door and keep a watch out for him—and my mom. If she gets here, I'll just pretend to be putting my bike away. But I'm relieved to see his car pull up, and I quickly help him throw the bags into the back of his SUV, hoping that Mom isn't about to show up. "You better get out of here fast," I warn him as he loads in his golf clubs.

"You're a champ, Kiera." He closes his hatch door then hurries to get in the driver's seat, waving to me and mouthing "Thank you!" I wave back, but as I push the down button on the garage door, watching his SUV disappear down the street, I feel a lump in my throat and the door stops with the thud of finality. This is the end of an era—the Josephsons have unraveled, and I doubt that anything will be able to patch them together again.

Twelve

MOIRA HAD CONVINCED HERSELF THAT Alex would come home from work as usual on Monday evening. And somehow she would make things right with him. To this end, she had stopped by Whole Foods and picked up all of his favorite dinner things—salmon, asparagus, pasta salad, and flourless chocolate cake. She even got a small bouquet of red roses and a bottle of Merlot. She wasn't a fan of heavy red wine, but Alex preferred it. And tonight was about making amends to him. Certainly, it wouldn't be easy to apologize—especially since she still believed he was more to blame than she—but if this was what it took to put this back together, she would swallow her pride and do it.

But as she parked in the garage, she noticed that Alex's golf clubs were gone. She felt a wave of concern as she carried the groceries inside. Alex didn't normally golf early in the week. But she tried to suppress a nagging voice warning her that all was not well. Alex had been gone since Saturday night. Surely he would be missing the comforts of his home by now.

The house seemed quieter than usual as she put away the groceries. She felt the chill of desertion, abandonment, death...but tried to shake it off. Determined not to succumb to negativity, she turned on some quiet music and opened the bottle of wine so it could breathe. Then she put the roses in a vase and got out two of her best crystal goblets and set them next to the wine bottle on the breakfast bar. Very pretty...and inviting. She wanted Alex to see this as soon as he entered the kitchen. Then she hurried to change out of her work clothes, into something more feminine. With Maddie gone and Kiera's aloof ways, this evening could be almost as if she and Alex were home alone. She would make him feel as if they were alone.

But as soon as she entered the master suite, Moira knew that something was different. The door to Alex's closet was ajar and, upon opening it, she saw that it had been stripped nearly clean. Only a few wintry items remained. Moira looked through his bureau to see that it had been emptied too. Going into the bathroom, she saw that his shaving and shower things were gone as well. When had he done this?

"Kiera!" she yelled as she raced up the stairs, pounding on her door.

"What is it?" Kiera pulled out her earbuds, staring at Moira with wide eyes and what Moira suspected was a trace of guilt.

"When was your father here?" she demanded.

Kiera shrugged. "A while ago."

"So you were home when he came?"

She shrugged again. "Yeah."

"And you witnessed him taking his belongings but didn't bother to let me know."

Kiera glanced away, a clear sign she was completely in the know about this.

"Kiera? I asked you a question." Moira grabbed Kiera's arm.

"I didn't think it was my responsibility to inform you of what your husband is doing," Kiera said in a wooden tone.

"You saw that he was moving out of our home, but you didn't think I should be informed of it?"

"I figured you probably knew."

Moira grabbed Kiera's other arm, forcing her to look at her. "I'll bet you helped him." Kiera tried to pull away, but Moira tightened her grip, narrowing her eyes. "You did, didn't you—you probably—"

"Let me go!" Kiera jerked away.

"You're probably glad he left!" Moira screamed at her.

"Leave me alone!" Kiera stepped back. "Get out of my room!"

"You don't own this room, Kiera. You're occupying it for now, but I own this house and—"

"*Fine!* You want me to go, Mom? I'm happy to leave you. Just like everyone else has left you—Hannah and Maddie and Dad. Now it's my turn. And then you can be all alone with your big wonderful house? Is that what you want?" Kiera let a foul word fly.

And Moira slapped her—hard.

"Don't you dare start using that kind of language in my house!" she shouted at Kiera. "I will not tolerate it!"

Kiera's dark eyes grew wide as she held her hand to her cheek, but she said nothing, only stepped back as if afraid that Moira might slap her again. And suddenly Moira felt like a real monster. "I—I—I didn't mean to do that," she stammered. "I—uh—I'm just so—"

"Never mind," Kiera said sharply. "Just go. Please, leave me alone and I'll pack my stuff and go. Dad said I can stay with him and—"

"No!" Moira yelled. "You don't have to go. Just don't talk to me like that." She put her face closer to Kiera. "Just treat me with some respect. That's all I ask. A little respect. Is that too much?"

"Whatever." Kiera's expression was smoldering—perhaps she wanted to strike back. But she just turned away and, with arms crossed, stared out her window, waiting for Moira to leave.

Moira didn't know what more to say as she quietly closed the door behind her. She knew that it was wrong to hit Kiera. But Kiera knew better than to talk like that—and Kiera knew that Moira was stressed out right now. Such a scene would've never happened with Hannah. Moira's eyes filled as she thought about how her older daughter would've handled this situation. She would've wrapped her arms around Moira and comforted her. Then she would've helped come up with a solution to get her dad to come home. Of course, if Hannah were still here, none of this would be happening.

Moira grabbed the bottle of Merlot and a goblet and carried it to the bedroom. So this was it. Alex was done. Moira was on her own. Why had she expected anything more? She filled her goblet full then went to get a Xanax. So much for her resolve not to take any more escape pills. In fact, unless her memory failed, she had another bottle of pain pills somewhere. Some oxycodone…from before. She'd hidden them in a winter handbag, just in case she'd need them again someday.

Well, she needed them now.

By the end of the week, Moira knew she was a complete and adept failure. And *failure* was not a word that a Type A personality normally used in reference to herself. But as Moira picked up a refill for her Xanax prescription, she knew it was true. For starters, she was a failure as a mom—as simple as one, two, and three. One, she'd lost a daughter to death…and a death that could've been prevented. Two, she'd lost a daughter to her mother-in-law for the summer… and possibly longer if Moira didn't pull herself together. And three, she'd lost Kiera to something Moira couldn't even explain. Sometimes Moira blamed her mother for Kiera—like faulty DNA. And there was no denying that Kiera resembled her maternal grandmother. Maybe that was why they just couldn't seem to get along.

Whatever the case, Kiera hadn't spoken to her all week. Not since the slapping incident. But hadn't Moira apologized? Shouldn't Kiera have understood the stress Moira was dealing with? Kiera was just stubborn and spoiled, and Moira hadn't bothered to call her on it. She convinced herself that Kiera's aloofness was partly related to the fact that she'd managed to get some kind of a job. Judging by the quirky uniform she wore as she rode off on her bike each morning, Kiera was probably waiting tables at that Australian restaurant or something. Well, fine—maybe she should start paying rent. They would need it.

Because, besides being a failure as a mother, Moira realized she was also a failure as a wife. Alex seemed to have left for good. And why not—hadn't she told him to go? For all she knew, he was filing papers right now. But she knew a divorce would be a financial disaster for her. Even with alimony, she'd have to make a lot of changes. Because after today's meeting at the real estate office, Moira felt fairly certain she was about to become unemployed.

As Moira tucked her refilled Xanax prescription safely in her big designer bag, along with a new bottle of oxycodone and Tylenol 3, she knew that she wasn't just a failure at motherhood, marriage, and career—she was a failure as a human being too. Because even more than the last time—after she'd disciplined herself to get free from her dependence on opioids following Hannah's death—Moira knew she needed pills as well as alcohol to simply put one foot in front of the other these days. If things had been bad then, they were way worse now.

In the past couple of days, mindful that she still had health insurance, Moira had turned to her shrink, general practitioner, gynecologist, and dentist. Playing the bereaved mother card, complaining of her old ruptured disk pain, debilitating menstrual cramps, and a toothache, she had accumulated enough pills to keep herself sedated for a while. She told herself it was only for the weekend. That she simply needed a break. She'd get some rest and escape her stress. Then perhaps by Monday, she would be stronger. She would get it together. She would show them that she was ready to work, maybe even sell a house or two.

But as she pulled into the garage, she knew the truth. She'd been down this dead-end road before. Pills and booze were a temporary fix that only made things worse. Sure, they might make you forget...for a while. But then what? As she went into the house, she knew she didn't really care.

Why should she?

Thirteen

AFTER MY FIRST WEEK OF PLAYING PARK counselor at Greenwood, I wonder what I've gotten myself into. Oh, I like the kids well enough. Most of them anyway—some are real brats. But it's been noisy and nonstop and nonsensical. It's hard to think sometimes. And even though labor law demands we take breaks, it's a joke if we actually get one. So by quitting time on Friday, I feel slightly euphoric. Like let me outta here! I feel like I could sleep all weekend.

For the last four days, I've painted rocks and faces and a basecoat on the shed which will get its mural next week. I've played box hockey, four-square, soccer and dodge-ball—as well as hopscotch and freeze-tag and kick-the-can and other childish games that no self-respecting sixteen-year-old wants to get caught doing. And I've strummed my guitar and taught camp songs and even made sand-castles. And it's exhausting.

As we lock up the shed, it's a relief that the park is nearly empty of kids. That's not exactly typical since we usually have a few hangers-on—kids make up all sorts of excuses not to go home like we encourage them to do when we leave. But thanks to the unbearable heat wave that's come on full force, and the fact that Bernard and I turned off the Slip'N Slide and cooling sprinkler about fifteen minutes ago, instructing the kids to go home and drink plenty of fluids, the park feels like a ghost-town. And I'm so ready for a weekend off. Except for one thing—or rather two things—Sheena and Sicily. I feel seriously sad to see the two little girls trudging down the street to their house.

For whatever reason, these two sisters immediately at-tached themselves to me on my first day here. Sheena is seven and Sicily is five, and this pair spends every day, usually the whole day, here at the park. Usually right by my side or nearby. By Friday, I know more about these girls than I care to. Their house is the shabby pink one with the broken front window and beat-up black Toyota parked in the front yard—so "Mom don't get a ticket for being on the street," Sheena told me. I know their mom stays home with a new baby and their dad's in prison. It seems obvious that Sheena and Sicily are pretty much on their own. But strangely enough, they don't even seem to realize how neglected they are. And as trite as it sounds, it breaks my heart.

"Want a ride?" Bernard asks me as I kneel down to unlock my bike.

I squint into the bright sun behind him and wonder if he's blind or just dumb. Does he honestly think he can fit my bike and me onto the compact car he usually drives to work? "Uh, I have my bike—as usual."

"And, not *as usual*, I drove my dad's pickup today." He grins like the joke's on me. "And, in case you haven't noticed, it's nearly a hundred degrees right now. Why don't you let me give you a lift?"

"Okay." And I'm barely standing when he picks up my bike and carries it over to an old blue pickup. "Thanks," I mutter as I get into the cab.

"Sorry, it's so hot in here." He cranks down the window. "And the windows aren't electric. And the AC doesn't work too well." He chuckles as he starts the engine. "Maybe you'll wish you were on your bike after all."

"No, this is probably better than heat stroke." I roll down my window, looking toward the little pink house as Sheena and Sicily go inside.

"Sad, isn't it?" Bernard says as he backs out.

"I've been seriously thinking about calling Child Protective Services," I confess. "Except that, according to what our handbook says, I might not have enough evidence to make a claim."

"Well, it's obvious that they're dirty. But most of the kids around here seem pretty scruffy. Especially at the end of the day. Hey, maybe we should give them bars of soap before they run through the sprinkler next time."

I can't help but snicker.

"So what kind of evidence do you have?" he asks.

"I'm not sure. I've asked them about food in the house. Sheena says they eat a lot of cereal, but it sounds a little sketchy. And they're always so hungry by lunchtime."

"I wonder if they have any other family around." Bernard slows for a light. "The mom might be overwhelmed."

"Yeah, I asked about that, and Sheena told me there's a Grandma Jeannie in Mayville. And she sounds nice. I wish I had her number."

"You probably don't know her name. I mean, besides Jeannie."

"Well, the girls' last name is Kooster—with two Os. But that doesn't necessarily mean that's their grandmother's name." Just the same I pull out my phone and open the white pages. "You think there could possibly be a Jeannie Kooster in Mayville?"

"Worth a try."

I do a quick search and am surprised to find a Rod and Jean Kooster in Mayville. I tell Bernard and he suggests I try it. When a woman answers, I'm flustered. "Hello, are you Jeannie Kooster?"

"Yes, who is this?"

"Do you have two granddaughters—Sheena and Sicily?"

"Yes, but tell me who is this? Are the girls okay?"

"Yes, they're okay. I mean, for now." I try to sound older. "But there's some concern for their welfare and—"

"Who is this?" she asks again.

"A concerned neighbor," I say with what I hope sounds like authority. "And the girls appear to be neglected and perhaps aren't getting enough food. We would hate to report this to CPS if there's a family member who could help out first. We understand there's a new baby and an incarcerated father—"

"Damien is innocent," the woman declares.

"So are Sheena and Sicily," I tell her. "And although they get some help through the free lunch program and the parks and recreation, they might be hungry during the weekend."

"Thank you for calling," she says with what sounds like sincerity. "I think I will drive over there and check on them. I appreciate your concern."

"Well, I didn't want to call CPS. Not yet anyway. I will if things don't improve." I notice now that Bernard has pulled over and is listening with interest.

"Yes, I understand. Thank you for taking the time to contact me."

By the time I end the call, my hands are shaking slightly and I turn to Bernard. "Was I wrong to do that?" I ask with uncertainty.

"No, I think you handled it really well. I'm proud of you."

"Why did you pull over?" I ask. "It's not like you were on the phone."

He chuckles. "I don't know where you live."

"Oh, yeah."

"In fact, I actually know very little about you. It's been such a busy-crazy week, we've barely had time to talk. I don't even know your last name."

"Josephson." I nod to him. "And yours?"

"Meyers."

I stick out my hand. "Bernard Meyers, nice to meet you."

He grins. "The pleasure's all mine."

I tell him where I live, and he begins to drive again. "I like this truck," I say. "I think it's cool that it's older."

"It's a 1968 Chevy," he says. "My dad's baby."

"What about the other car?"

"That's mine. But it's getting new tires today so Dad drove it. He's got a tire shop downtown and—"

"Meyers Tires? Is that it?"

He makes a sheepish grin. "Yep."

"I'm surprised you don't want to work there. Might be easier than chasing a bunch of neglected street urchins around."

"My dad would agree with you." He turns down my street. "But I don't. I worked there one summer in high school, and it felt like the smell of tire rubber seeped into my skin. To this day, I can barely go inside the store without feeling sick to my stomach."

"My house is just two houses down." I point it out, but as he slows down, I see my mom's car coming from the other direction. "But, uh, just keep going, okay?"

"Huh?"

"Just keep going. You can drop me off on the next block." I scrunch down in the seat, hoping that Mom hasn't seen me.

"Are you a spy or something?" he asks as he drives past my house.

"No. I just didn't want to cross paths with my mom."

"Oh…I see. Embarrassed to be seen with someone like me?"

"No, of course not," I snap at him.

"Okay." He sounds slightly hurt, and I feel guilty.

After a couple of blocks, I ask him to let me out.

"Hey, if you're not eager to go home, we could go get Slurpees."

"*Slurpees?*" I repeat in a snarky tone. "Seriously—how old are you—*eight?*"

"Even if I was eighty-eight, I'd appreciate a Slurpee on a hot day like this. And I wouldn't be too embarrassed to say so."

"You know, it actually sounds kinda good."

Before long, we're seated at a grimy plastic picnic table on the shady side of the neighborhood 7-Eleven, sipping on blue Slurpees. "This is pretty refreshing," I admit sheepishly. "I don't think I've had one of these in years."

"Too sophisticated for Slurpees?" he teases.

"Apparently not."

"Well, I've noticed that you don't eat meat." His brows arch. "I'm guessing vegetarian? Hopefully not vegan?"

I frown. "Why *hopefully not?*"

He shrugs. "Oh, it's just that most vegans tend to be such food snobs. Like they're superior to the rest of us. Whereas vegetarians, I've found, are generally easier to get along with."

"Interesting." I frown.

"So you *are* vegan?" He looks disappointed.

"Well, not religiously. I went vegetarian about a year ago…then vegan last winter."

"Any special reason why?" He studies me closely, but I simply shrug. "It's just that I've found some people have an explanation. Like they toured a hotdog factory or worked in a smelly dairy or lost a beloved pet."

I take in a quick breath then glance down at my drink, poking my straw up and down in the slush as if absorbed by the process.

"Really?" His tone softens. "You lost a pet?"

I look up at him, realizing it's probably best to just get this out in the open. "A sister. Last January."

"Oh." He looks slightly shocked. "I'm sorry."

"Thanks."

"Well, I know how it feels to lose a loved one," he says quietly. "Takes time to get over it."

"Do you ever get over it?" I stare at him, wishing he

had some answer to make it better, but knowing that's impossible.

"I guess not. But it gets better with time. I was twelve when my mom died. I was pretty devastated. But it does get easier."

"I'm sorry," I say. "I mean for your loss."

"Thanks, but I'm okay now." He peers curiously at me. "So was your sister older or younger than you?"

"Older. But not by much. We were what some people call Irish twins. Only fourteen months apart." I don't tell him that I was unplanned and unwanted. TMI. "But Hannah and I were as different as night and day." I don't admit that I was night and Hannah was day.

"Your last name is Josephson?" He frowns. "Roosevelt High?"

I nod glumly.

"Your sister was Hannah Josephson." It's more statement than question.

"You knew her?"

"Not really. I mean I knew *who* she was. I was a year ahead of her. But I remember her as a sweet girl. Real pretty too."

"Yeah, she was the beauty, I was the brains." I laugh without humor. "Although I'm doing my best to change that now. My grades slipped this last semester."

"That's understandable. But I'm sure that'll get better for you next year."

"Maybe." I set down my cup then slowly shake my

head. "Although it pretty much feels like everything in my life is sliding steadily downhill." I sigh. "Well, except for this summer job. I actually kind of like it. I mean, it's hard work. But it's pretty cool."

"I like it too." Now he tells me that he might get a degree in social work or counseling. "My dad wants me to major in business and take over the tire company, but that's not going to happen."

"Not if you've developed an allergy to rubber."

"For sure." He pauses as a couple of tween girls hover nearby, simply watching as they make rude comments about our park uniforms.

"We're actually undercover police," I tell them with a serious expression, "here to keep surveillance on juvenile delinquents like you two."

"So you better watch it," Bernard says in a deep voice, and the girls scurry away.

"Good work." I grin as I polish off the last of my Slurpee. "And thanks for this. Nice idea."

"And it's been nice getting to know you better." He tosses his empty cup into the nearby trash can. "Want me to give you a ride home yet, or are you in some kind of stand-off with your mom?"

I roll my eyes as I lob my cup into the can. "You don't want to know."

"Actually, I do. But now I've got a hankering for ice cream. I suppose I can't tempt a vegan like you into some soft serve vanilla?"

I let out a long sigh. "Vanilla ice cream just happens to be my weakness." I hold up my hands in surrender. "So, hey, maybe being vegan is overrated. I've been thinking about returning to plain vegetarian anyway."

He grins. "Two soft serves coming up."

As he goes back into 7-Eleven, I'm torn. On one hand, I can't believe I'm giving up on veganism for ice cream. On the other hand, I've been looking for an excuse for a while now. And I know life will get easier for me if I let it go. And, considering all things, easier sounds pretty good.

Bernard returns with our soft serve and sits down. "So, tell me about your mom."

And like an exchange, as he hands me my cone I pour out the story of how our family is falling completely apart. I tell him all the dirty details of our recent dysfunctions. The only thing I leave out is Hannah.

"It's not unusual for families to go through hard times after a death," he says somberly.

"You sound just like my counselor." I resist the urge to plant my cone onto his forehead.

"Thank you."

"It wasn't a compliment."

He frowns. "Well, if I *were* your counselor, I'd ask you whether or not you or your family members are blaming themselves for Hannah's death."

"Why?"

"Because it's a normal reaction. I even felt guilty for my mom's death—and she died of cancer. But as a kid, I thought maybe if I'd been better or smarter or nicer...well, maybe she'd have gotten well. I realize it makes no sense now, but I honestly felt like that back then."

"Yeah, I get that. But in my family, I think it's more about blame than guilt. It's like everyone blames everyone else for what happened. And maybe legitimately too." I'm thinking this conversation needs some fast redirection. Bernard is hitting too close to home—too close for my comfort. And I'm tempted to tell him about reading my dead sister's diary, but I think I'd rather die than have anyone know about that. "So, anyway, my mom and I have had a pretty rough week," I say quickly. "She's a mess since my dad left. And I'm mostly trying to avoid her. That's why I didn't want to go home earlier. Didn't want to take a chance of a confrontation. But she's had enough time to bury herself in her room by now. It's probably safe to go."

"Whenever you're ready." He stands, still holding his half-eaten cone.

Although I'm sort of disappointed to leave, I stand too. After all, I can't expect him to hang with me all night. He's probably as eager to hit the shower as I am. "Thanks for the Slurpee and ice cream," I say. "And for listening."

"Well, I figure if we have to work together all summer, we should at least have a basic understanding of each other." He whistles as he leads the way to his pickup.

I glance at him as we get into the cab. What he just said sounds so clinical and impersonal. Was that all this was to him? A "basic understanding"? Kind of like an interview? Was it naïve to hope that he wanted to be my friend? Or just pathetic? But I realize he's a college guy and I'm only sixteen. He probably wants to keep it professional. And who can blame him for wanting to establish some boundaries, keep a safe distance? Especially after hearing about my messed-up family.

Fourteen

JUST LIKE EVERY OTHER DAY THIS WEEK, the house is so quiet that I question whether my mom is really home. Except that I know she is. I welcomed her absent-presence the past few days. It allowed me to make myself some dinner and launder my uniform and a few other necessary tasks without her breathing down my neck. But realizing I have a whole weekend to ramble around in a house that feels dead and empty makes me feel incredibly lonely.

I haven't read Hannah's diary for days. I think about it a lot, but the idea of sitting down with it again is overwhelming. Besides that, I know it must be hotter than heck in the tree house. But finally, after I've had my shower and consumed a bowl of ramen noodles and an apple, I can't think of anything but Hannah...and her diary. I want to know how she handled things after her horrid experience with nasty Maxwell Harter. How did she go on? And how did she manage to keep up such a brave front for all of us? I would never be able to do that.

It's just getting dusky when I slip out and go up into the tree house. With the windows propped open, it's actually not too bad up there. I have a flashlight and some pillows I swiped from the family room. I lean back and, bracing myself for more pain, I start to read. I work through several pages of disturbing rants. Hannah was so hurt and so lost, it's almost unbearable to read. When I think of times that I've been wounded or isolated by friends or family, it seems like nothing compared to what Hannah went through. And yet none of us knew. Even though I went to the same high school, I was completely oblivious. In fact, it makes me wonder if she might've been wrong about "everyone knowing."

Hannah seems to take a break from writing in March. Maybe it got too painful for her since she really seemed to let her hair down in her diary. But her next entry in early April, while not obsessing over her bad experience, seems darker than ever.

I feel like I have nothing to live for. Nothing to look forward to. No one to really care about and no one who really cares about me. Oh, I know that Mom loves me—in her funny way. But it's like she wants me to be a replica of her. And I really don't want that. I used to like youth group and my old friends. But it feels like I have alienated myself from them too. It doesn't help to see that Haley is going after Wyatt. I wish I could turn back the clock. And then again, I don't. It's like something was broken. Probably me. But now it's worse than broken. It's dead. That's it. I feel like I'm dead. Oh, I go around with my perpetual smile and I try to act like I'm perfectly fine—like a smiley face robot girl. But underneath my façade I feel dead. And if there were a way to end this thing—without hurting anyone—I would gladly do so. But I think of Maddie and my parents and even Kiera, who acts like she hates me… I know it would be selfish to take my life. But if something else ended it, maybe that would make it easier.

I can barely see the next page through my tears, and my flashlight is dimming anyway, so I close the diary, tuck it back into its hiding place and sneak back into the house. A small part of me—probably a piece from my childhood—wants to run to my mother and tell her what I've just learned about Hannah. But I know no good would come of it. Besides being enraged at me for stealing her diary, my mom would probably really fall apart if she knew the truth about Hannah.

But as I lay awake in the dark on my bed, I wonder… did Hannah intentionally run into the tree that night? Was that her way of making her death look like an accident? And even if it was her "unselfish" choice to die like that—what good did it do? The pain she left behind was just as real as if she'd downed a bottle of pills. What difference did it make? For the first time since Hannah died, I feel angry at her. If she really did take her own life, I'm not sure I'll ever be able to forgive her. The wreckage she left behind was much more than a flattened car. So much more.

I'm still frustrated the next morning. Still angry at Hannah for dying. Especially if she did it on purpose. As I rattle around in the kitchen, I remember Saturday mornings from the past. It was Daddy Breakfast Morning, and we always looked forward to a hearty breakfast of bacon and eggs and pancakes. Although I've put vegan behind me, I almost think I could cast vegetarian aside too—for bacon. Instead, I'm indulging in eggs, which means I'm a pescetarian. But I haven't had eggs in months. And since my stomach didn't rebel against the dairy I consumed yesterday with Bernard, I'm not overly worried about eggs.

"What are you doing?" my mom demands just as I'm attempting to scramble some eggs.

"Fixing breakfast," I say without looking at her.

"Eggs?" She comes over and stares blankly into the pan. Standing there in her bathrobe and bare feet, I wonder if she realizes how haggard she looks. Her hair's sticking out all over, and she's got ugly black smudges of eye-makeup ringing her eyes. My beautiful mother is a mess.

"Yeah." I hold the pan in front of her, knowing that she won't appreciate how they're a little crusty and brown around the edges. "You want some?"

"Yuck. No."

I dump them onto a plate then turn to look at her. "Are you okay?"

"Okay?" She frowns as she pours herself a cup of coffee from the pot I made earlier, just like I've been making it every morning this week—*thank you very much, Kiera.*

"Yeah, no offense, but you look a little raggedy."

"Thanks a lot." She turns to stare out the window above the sink, holding her coffee mug with both hands. I notice they're trembling.

"Just saying." And then, not wanting to eat my breakfast with an audience, I pour a glass of orange juice and take my food up to my room to dine in solitude. I've never seen my mom look this bad before. Not even after Hannah died. I feel fairly certain she's turned to pills and booze. And I have no idea what I should do about it. Or if it should even be my problem. As I finish eating, I feel anger coming on at Dad now. The image of the captain jumping from the sinking ship comes at me again. What right does he have to bail like that?

As I go downstairs, I feel unexpectedly sympathetic toward my mom. No wonder she's a wreck. Maybe I should try harder to understand. I'm just setting my dishes in the sink when she rushes into the kitchen with a wild look in her eyes. "Don't leave those there, Kiera!"

"I wasn't—"

"I'm not your maid, you know. I won't clean up after you anymore. You take care of your messes." She points to the pan still on the stove. "And don't forget to clean that up too. Not just the pan either. Clean the stove too."

"In case you haven't noticed, I have been cleaning up lately," I tell her in a slightly snotty tone.

"Your idea of clean and my idea are worlds apart, Kiera. Of everyone in this family, we all know you're the biggest slob."

"Looks like you're trying to take over that title." My feeble attempt at humor falls short as Mom narrows her raccoon eyes.

"Don't you go provoking me, Miss Smart-mouth. I've got my reasons for this."

"Sorry." I pick up the pan and carry it to the sink. So much for feeling sorry for her. My mom's a witch who probably deserves it if everyone leaves her. Including me as soon as I get the chance.

As I scrub out the pan, she continues to jab at me, pointing out what I'm doing wrong, which seems to be everything until I can't take it anymore. "Sorry I don't measure up to your high standards." I hand her the dripping pan. "Why don't you show me how it's done." Then before she can respond, I head out through the garage, get my bike, and take off. I wish I had work today.

After I ride around awhile, I also wish I had my phone with me. Although I wonder why. It's not like I have a friend I could go hang with. Life sucks! But not enough to kill myself. I wonder again—is that what Hannah did? All over a stupid boy. I've never honestly wanted to kill anyone, but I think if I got the chance, if someone put a gun in my hand and Maxwell Harter in front of me—I think I could pull the trigger.

I eventually wind up in front of the Smyth house—where my dad is "baching it" with Larry. Hopefully they're not sleeping in this morning, which isn't likely. What is likely is that they'll be out playing golf. Fully expecting no one to answer, I lean on the doorbell and get ready to leave. But to my surprise, Larry opens the door.

"What have we here?" he says in a teasing tone. "Hey, Alex, look what the cat dragged in."

"Thanks." I push past him without waiting for an invitation.

"It's getting warm out there." Larry closes the door. "Maybe we should toss you in the pool, Kiera. You look a little hot around the collar." He chuckles like this is funny.

"Sorry to come without calling first," I say as Dad comes into the great room looking casual and comfortable in a t-shirt and shorts. "I was on my bike and didn't have my phone with me."

"That's okay." Dad towels his damp hair. "Larry doesn't mind, do you, Lar?"

"Not at all. I was just telling your dad it's been awfully quiet around here with Terri and the kids gone. Need someone to liven things up."

"I just took a swim in the pool," Dad tells me. "Refreshing."

"So I hear." I flop onto one of the barstools with a sigh.

"Is something wrong?" Dad asks with a furrowed brow.

"Mom." I'm not sure Dad wants his dirty laundry tossed around in front of his buddy. But he seems oblivious. Maybe he's already told Larry everything. Nice that he has someone to talk to.

"What's going on?" Dad presses.

"She's nuts, that's all."

"More so than usual?" Dad attempts a smile, but I can see through it.

"You want the truth?" I glance at Larry, and he apparently gets the hint as he excuses himself to go mow the lawn before it gets too hot.

"What's up, Kiera?" Dad looks concerned now.

"I know Mom's drinking 'cause I see the bottles in the trash, but I think she's mixing it with pills now."

Dad slowly nods. "Yeah, I'm aware of that."

"You're aware of that? But you leave her alone? I mean with just me? What am I supposed to do?"

"Do?" He uses his thumb to rub what looks like a coffee spill on the countertop.

"What if she ODs?" I ask. "Alcohol and opiates, Dad? Haven't you heard that can be lethal?"

He runs his hand through his damp hair and lets out a long sigh. "Do you think she needs a treatment program?"

I frown. "How would I know? I mean, it's probably not like she's addicted...yet. And anyway, I've heard that you can't just put people in treatment, they have to want to get better or it's useless. I watch Dr. Phil, you know."

"Then what do you want me to do?"

"I don't know." I hold up my hands. "But right now, it's starting to feel like Mom's my problem. I mean I'm the only one left—and she's pretty much a mess. What am I supposed to do?"

"Go about your life, Kiera. As much as you can anyway. Mom's an adult. She's responsible for herself. And, although you're *not* an adult, you seem to think you are. So enjoy your freedom and live your life. Go to work. Hang with your friends. Enjoy summer."

I roll my eyes. How can he be so clueless?

"What?" he demands.

"Nothing." I growl back at him. "Sorry I bothered you." I stand now, ready to storm out. But he grabs me by the shoulders, staring into my eyes. "I don't get you, Kiera. What do you want me to do?"

"Come home?" I try.

He releases me and slowly shakes his head. "That

won't help. In fact, it would probably just make it worse. She already was blaming me for her problems. If Moira is on her own, it might help her to take responsibility for her problems. Might help her to see things more clearly."

"How can she see anything clearly if she's doped up and wasted?"

"Maybe she'll see what a mess she's become and get sick of it. You know, like they say, maybe she'll hit rock bottom. And then maybe she'll face up to what's wrong and get some help."

"That's a lot of maybes."

"I know. But can't you see that those are your mom's problems? Not yours."

I want to declare that they're all of our problems, that we used to be a family, that we used to help each other, that it's not good to be all broken up like this. But I'm afraid I'll burst into tears if I go there.

"Now, what can I do to help you, honey?" He peers curiously at me. "Do you need money? I know you're working, but I'll bet you don't get paid for a while."

"Well, we're getting low on groceries and I doubt Mom will be making any runs to the store anytime soon."

Dad pulls out his wallet and hands me a generous handful of cash, which I pocket. "Anything else?" he asks with what seems genuine concern.

"I guess not."

He jerks his thumb over a shoulder toward the pool in the backyard. "You should invite some of your friends over. Larry keeps complaining about no one using the pool. That's why I took a swim this morning. But it was pretty nice. Almost makes me wish we'd put in a pool... before."

"Yeah." I feel a lump in my throat. *Before.* That sounds like a lifetime ago.

"So how's the job going? Did you start this week like you thought you would?"

"Yeah. It's going pretty good." I force a little smile. "I guess I like it okay."

"Hey, do you need something to drink? You look a little flushed. And you rode your bike over." He opens the fridge. "I just stocked it with some sodas yesterday."

"And beer," I point out a six-pack as I reach for a Sierra Mist.

"Hey, this is a bachelor pad." He grins.

I glance around the messy kitchen counters. "So I see."

"And really, Kiera, if it's that hard being with your mom right now, I could ask Larry about you staying here, but I don't—"

"No, that's okay. I'm mostly gone during the week because of work. But maybe I could hang here on weekends...sometimes. Like maybe later for a swim. That actually sounds kinda good."

"I wish you would."

We make small talk while I drink my soda, but it gets quiet, and I feel like maybe I should go. Not that I'm unwelcome, but I suddenly feel out of place in their bachelor pad. Still, I might take them up on the offer of hanging by the pool. Too bad I don't have a friend I could bring with me. That'd be nice. As I pedal back home, the sun is getting really hot and I'm wishing I'd jumped into Larry's pool with my clothes on.

As I wheel my bike into the garage, I notice Mom's car is gone. I vaguely wonder if she might be showing a house, but I can't imagine her going out in her current state and I doubt she could've pulled it together that fast. I see a bag of her empties by the backdoor. Maybe she's on a booze run. As I go inside, I get an idea. How about taking a quick peek at her medicine cabinet? If I'm going to be a housemate with an addict all summer, I might as well have some idea of what she's using. Just in case I need to call 911.

I literally gasp to see the row of prescription pill bottles on her bathroom counter. All lined up like Mom's running some kind of at-home pain clinic. I can't even imagine how she got them prescribed to her and don't really care to know. I quickly read the labels—specifically the dates and amount of pills in each bottle. I do a quick inventory and mental math to find most of the pills are still there. It's both a relief and a concern. Relieved that she hasn't taken more and become seriously addicted, and concerned that with all these pills—and alcohol—she could easily OD.

And so I do something that could land me in serious hot water. I grab some tissues and dump the pills onto it, leaving only a few in each bottle. According to the recommended dosage on the labels there's enough left to last a normal person a couple of weeks. But we're not dealing with normal here. I line the bottles up again, hopefully exactly like they were. Then I stuff the tissue-wrapped pill wads into my pocket and, making sure the coast is clear, I run up to my bathroom, where I'm about to flush them. I pause, realizing there could be hell to pay if Mom figures out that I dumped them like this. Not that I plan to give the pills back to her. Although she might kill me if I don't.

I vaguely wonder if I could dole them out slowly, less each day until she's clean and sober. Like a DIY rehab facility. Yeah, right. For the time I'll hide them. I dump the pills into an old Altoids tin which I run out to the tree house and stash along with the stolen diary—under the window sill where old secrets go to die.

Fifteen

I'M SO NERVOUS AFTER STEALING MOM'S pills that I can hardly breathe—and sweating like a pig, which might be from my bike ride. I'm headed for the shower, but so don't want to be around when Mom discovers what I've done. I can't even imagine the fit she could throw. Maybe I should hide all sharp objects. Instead, I grab my phone and backpack, which still has Hannah's bikini in it, and shove in a few necessities then make a clean getaway, pedaling my bike as fast as I can until I'm about a mile from home.

This time I call my dad before showing up on their doorstep and he sounds almost glad to hear my voice. "Larry and I were just heading out to play golf, but there's a key hidden under the big green flower pot on the front porch. He keeps it there for his kids." Dad pauses to talk to Larry. "He says to make yourself at home, just make sure to get the pizza off the ceiling before we get back." He laughs, and I hear Larry laughing too.

"Thanks, I'll keep that in mind."

"We're playing eighteen holes unless the heat gets to us."

"Have fun." I'm actually glad that they'll be gone. I need time to compose myself. And cool off in that pool. I also need time to compose a lie for my mom—for when she accuses me, which seems inevitable. Unless her mind is really messed up. It's possible she'll assume she's taken them. I wonder if she counts them. Or how she keeps track of what she's taken and when...and what keeps her from taking too many?

The key is right where Dad said it would be. And before long, I'm pulling Hannah's old swimsuit out, which smells a little rank after being damp in my backpack for more than a week, but I give it a good rinse in the powder-room sink and then, hoping the chlorine will help, I jump into the pool where I sit under water for as long as I can hold my breath, trying to think of a believable lie that will throw Mom off my trail. Finally, I decide to simply say that I've been at Larry's the whole while. Simple lies are easier to pull off.

Besides, I think as I float on an air mattress, maybe she won't even ask me. She might be too embarrassed to admit she's got so many prescriptions that she can't keep track of them. And if she does ask, I can feign shock that she's using opiates. I can ask why she's taking all those pills and suggest she needs professional help.

After about an hour of hanging in the pool, I feel surprisingly refreshed and relaxed…almost like a normal person. But when I go into the house, I hear my phone ringing and feel certain it's my mom. I nervously check, ready to ignore it. But I'm surprised to see it's Bernard. I nearly forgot that we exchanged numbers on my first day at work, just in case either of us was late or anything. I can't believe he's calling me.

"Hey, Bernard." With a towel wrapped around me, I perch on a barstool. "What's up?"

"Not much. But I thought you might like an update on the Kooster sisters."

"What do you mean?"

"Well, I happened to drive by there this morning and I saw a different car was parked in the driveway. Then I noticed an older woman inside. I think it must be the grandma."

"Oh, good. But how did you just happen to drive by there?"

He chuckles. "I guess I missed being at the park today."

"I sure don't. It's too hot to be in that park."

"I could get out the Slip'N Slide for you," he jokes.

"Thanks, but I just enjoyed a nice dip in the pool and I'm fine."

"No way? You have a pool? I'm jealous."

I explain about my dad staying at Larry's house and how I came over for the day. I figure, worst case scenario, Bernard could be an alibi for my mom. Not that I'm going there. "Hey, you could come over if you want," I say. "My dad told me I should invite a friend." I'm not about to admit I have no real friends. "I guess that includes you." I giggle like I'm twelve and immediately feel stupid.

"Seriously—you want me to come over?"

I tell myself to chill. It's not like this is a date. "Sure, why not," I use a casual tone, giving him the address. He says he'll be over around one. While I'm waiting for him to get here, I decide to do Dad and Larry a favor by cleaning up the kitchen. Too bad my mom can't see me as I empty and load the dishwasher then wipe down the countertops—without being told. Not that I'm anxious to cross paths with her anytime soon. In fact, I think I'll ask Dad about spending the night.

I try not to imagine what she'll do when she figures out what I've done. I know it won't be pretty. I wonder if I should cover my trail with a text to reinforce the illusion that I've been at Larry's this whole time. I carefully craft one—and it's not exactly a lie.

> FYI. Not that you care, but I'm spending weekend with Dad. You don't need to call the authorities and report me missing. Like you'd care.

As I hit send, I think it's just snarky enough to be credible. And now I turn off my phone and shove it into my backpack, along with any concerns about my mom. As I putter around the house, straightening up newspapers and fluffing pillows, I hate that I'm this excited about Bernard coming over. Really, this isn't anything but friends hanging together. To imagine something more is to invite trouble.

Get over yourself, I say as I put a fresh t-shirt over my swimsuit, which I plan to keep on while Bernard's here. It's not that I'm uncomfortable with my body exactly. I mean, I realize that I'm not as curvy as Hannah was—and I don't fill out her old bikini like she did. But I think I look okay. The t-shirt is simply because, unlike some girls I know, I'm not an exhibitionist.

It's nearly two when Bernard arrives, but I try to act like I haven't been waiting impatiently as I let him in. I see his dad's old pickup parked in front, and Bernard looks hot and flushed. "I had to fix a flat tire," he tells me as he comes in.

"On Mr. Meyers Tires' truck?" I tease.

"Yeah. Looks like I ran over a nail." He grins to see the pool out back. "I'm so ready for this." I tell him to go for it and without even answering, he's on his way, peeling off his sweaty t-shirt and kicking off his sandals. I watch with amusement as he carefully sets his glasses on the picnic table then cannonballs into the pool. Instead of joining him, like I'm compelled to do, I get myself a soda and meander outside. There, I linger on a lounge chair, casually sipping my drink until his taunts and splashes lure me into the pool. Then we laugh and play and tease with as much maturity as our Greenwood Park kids.

"Wanna race?" I challenge him.

"Only if you wanna lose," he shoots back.

So we line up on the deep end, agree to an over and back lap, and take off. By now Bernard knows that I'm highly competitive, but he doesn't know I'm a pretty good swimmer. And, even though Hannah used to tell me I shouldn't beat boys in athletics, I go full-throttle and win by a single stroke.

"Wow, you're good." Surprise shines in his eyes.

"Thank you," I say breathlessly. "You're not bad either." I climb out and go for my towel and slightly warm soda.

"Any more of those?" he asks as he climbs out.

Feeling like a negligent host, I go fetch him both a towel and a soda, and we settle onto lounge chairs. "Ah, this is the life," I say in an affected tone. "Now where is that cabana boy with my lunch?"

"Yeah." He nods. "Good idea."

I remember the money Dad gave me—and the fact that I've given up my vegan ways. "Hey, I could get pizza delivered. Interested?"

His eyes light up, and I tell him lunch is on me, as long as he doesn't complain about my choice. He gladly agrees, and I get my phone to call it in. Of course, there are several angry texts from my mom, but ignoring them, I place my order, turn off my phone, and try not to think about Mom as I go back outside.

"Everything okay?" he asks as I move my chaise into the shade.

"I guess so."

Bernard moves his chaise over too. "You seem upset."

"It's just my mom and me again. We had a fight this morning. That's why I came over here. She sent me a bunch of mad texts."

"That's too bad."

"Yeah. I guess I'll just stay over here until she cools off." I shake my head. "She's really a mess." Then, not wanting to talk about her, I set down my soda can and head for the diving board. "Here goes nothing," I say as I hold my hands high. Then, although I haven't attempted this trick for a while, I do a handstand on the edge of the board then flip over and land in the pool. When I come out of the water, Bernard is clapping.

"You're a real athlete," he tells me as I shake water out of my hair.

"I used to think I was." I climb out and sit on the edge. "But I kind of gave it up."

"Why?" He sits beside me, and we both dangle our feet in the cool blue water.

"I don't know. Lost interest. Took up art and music instead."

"How'd you get to be such a good swimmer?"

"I was on swim team for a few years. From about ten to thirteen."

"Why'd you quit?"

"I guess I wasn't that into it." I shrug. "And to be honest, I only took it up because Hannah did. That was back when we got along—if Hannah did something, I wanted to do it too. But when she quit swim team, I actually wanted to stick with it."

"But you didn't?"

"My mom didn't like making the trips for just one of us." I sigh. "Although she probably would've gladly kept it up if only Hannah wanted to."

"Did your mom favor Hannah?"

I just nod.

"So why did Hannah quit?"

"Honestly—I think it was because I was getting better times. But she said it was because swimming ruined her hair. She was a blonde, and the chlorine turned it kinda green. Her friends probably teased her. And she was getting all into clothes and friends and popularity. Swim team didn't fit her image anymore. I didn't really have an image—or blonde hair." I ruffle my fingers through my weird cropped cut.

"I like your hair."

I laugh and, feeling awkward and self-conscious, slide into the water and swim beneath the surface to the other side of the pool. Bernard jumps in, and suddenly we're playing and joking like kids again. But something seems slightly different too. Okay, I could be seeing something that's not there, but I honestly think that Bernard likes me. And, as nice as that feels, it concerns me. I don't think it's a good idea to fall in love with a coworker. I doubt that Val would approve. Still, it feels nice.

I hear a buzzer and realize that it's probably connected to the doorbell. "Our pizza," I exclaim as I climb out and hurry to the front door. Dripping wet, I hand the pizza guy my soggy money and then carry my prize back out by the pool. I haven't had a real pizza in months, and I'm literally salivating. Or maybe just wet. Anyway, we get more sodas and pig out on pizza until there's only one slice left. "I'm full." I shove the box toward him. "You can have it."

He doesn't refuse, and I watch with satisfaction as he polishes it off. Then realizing that I probably left puddles of water in the house, I take my towel inside and dry off the floors. I'm just finishing when Dad and Larry come in.

"Hey, I like this," Larry says. "A girl who scrubs the floors. We might need to keep you around, Kiera."

"She never scrubbed floors in my house," Dad teases.

I explain about answering the pizza delivery and that I've had my friend and coworker over. I can feel my cheeks blushing—or maybe it's from the sun—as I introduce them to Bernard.

"Thanks for letting me cool off in your pool," Bernard says to Larry. "I had to change a tire in the hot sun, and I think that swim might've saved my life."

Then, as Dad and Larry both say that's where they're headed, Bernard gathers up his stuff and announces he needs to get home. And, although I'd really like him to stay, it's a relief he's going. I'm just not ready for this. Not yet anyway. And not here.

I go back outside to watch Dad and Larry in the pool until I get so warm that I join them. Then Dad starts bragging about what a swimmer I am and we start having races. It's fun to hear the pride in Dad's voice after I soundly beat Larry. It's almost like going back in time…back to before our lives were turned upside down. All in all, it's a very good day. Well, except for the business related to Mom, but I'm trying not to think about that.

After Larry goes into the house, I decide to make my plea with my dad. I start by attempting to confess that I might've done something bad—*very* bad. His brow creases with fatherly concern, and I quickly explain about stealing my mom's pills.

"You're kidding." He towels off his hair with a slightly shocked expression.

"I only did it because I'm worried about her." I frown. "Was it wrong?"

"Well, to be honest, I don't know. I mean, it was wrong to go into your mom's bathroom and mess with her stuff, Kiera. Of course, that's wrong. But it's also wrong that she's got that many pills from all those doctors—and it's wrong that she's abusing them."

"I know. I'm really worried she could OD, Dad." Now

I tell him about all the empty bottles. "And not just wine either. There were vodka bottles in the bag too."

"Well, this is worse than I thought." He tosses his used towel in the wicker hamper by the door.

"So anyway, Mom sort of thinks I've been here all day. I mean, I sort of led her to believe that. Not that I lied exactly. But I gave the impression that I'm spending the weekend with you. So, if you don't mind, I'd like to stay overnight. I can sleep on a couch or even the floor. Is that okay?"

"It's okay with me. Larry probably won't mind. But this thing with your mom, Kiera." He slowly shakes his head. "What a mess. She could be really mad at you."

Now I confess I didn't dispose of her pills. "I could give them back to her if you—"

"No! Don't do that."

"What then?"

He sighs. "Well, I guess we'll have to wait and see. Maybe she's so dopy she won't realize any pills are missing."

"She knows." I tell him about the texts.

"And she suspects you?"

I just nod, wishing I'd never done it.

"Well, I'll back you, Kiera. I'm not sure I'll need to. But if it comes down to it, I'll tell her you've been here, that you're spending the weekend with me."

"Hopefully you won't need to."

"Hopefully." He opens the door. "I'm heading for the shower—followed by a nap." There must be something in the air—or just the heat and the exercise—but the house gets very quiet, and I think we must've all fallen asleep, but I wake to the sound of a doorbell ringing and someone pounding on the door. Since I was asleep on the great room couch, I'm the first one to get there, but Dad and Larry aren't far behind.

"You better come with me," my mom bellows as soon as I've opened the door. "Right now, young lady. March!" She grabs me by the arm, pointing to her car that's still running and parked diagonally in the driveway.

"No," I say firmly. "I'm spending the weekend with Dad."

"You were in my bathroom, Kiera. You're a dirty little thief!" She shouts so loudly that I'm sure she's been drinking. She starts dragging me out the door.

"Let go of her, Moira," Dad says in a quiet but firm tone.

Mom looks up at him then scowls. "You stay out of this. It's none of your business."

"Kiera's my daughter, which makes her my business." Dad is holding onto my other arm, making me feel like a rope in a tug-a-war.

"Let her go!" Mom shouts. "I'm taking her home."

"No, you're not." Dad reaches over to pry her fingers from my arm. "She's not going anywhere with you while you're in that condition."

"She stole something from me!" Mom shouts as I finally can jerk my arm free of her grip.

"Look, Moira, if you want to talk in a rational, civilized manner, you can come inside. But if you're going to act like a crazy woman, you should just go home."

"Not without my daughter."

"She's my daughter too." Dad pushes me behind him.

"You abandoned her!" Mom shouts. "Just like you abandoned me!"

"I'd like you to leave, Moira." Dad is trying to close the door, but Mom is still pounding on it.

"Let me in," she cries. "You big coward. You can't run out and then take Kiera too. You've taken everything from me."

I glance over at Larry to see he looks truly alarmed. "I'm sorry," I mutter as my mom continues to scream at my dad.

"Let me say something." Larry pulls the door open wide, and I can see my mom is surprised. "Look, Moira," he says in a tough voice. "If you don't leave right now, I'm going to call the police. Do you understand?"

Mom's eyes grow wide, but she steps back. "I—I just want my daughter," she whimpers. "That's all. I need Kiera to come with me."

"Kiera wants to stay here," Dad declares. "Go home, Moira."

"But I—"

"I'm about to dial the police." Larry holds up his phone. "Unless you leave, I'm calling them—right now."

My mom shakes a fist in the air then lets loose with

some choice words—words that she'd freak over if I used them. But at least she leaves. We all stand on the porch watching as she backs her car out too fast, ripping through a corner of Larry's lawn before she tears down the street.

"Sorry, Lar," Dad says glumly. "I'll fix that sod for you."

"Wow." Larry shakes his head. "Who'd a thunk?"

"Yeah…awkward." Dad looks embarrassed.

"Do you think she'll be okay?" I ask quietly.

"Who knows—who cares?" Dad's tone grows irritated as we go inside. "Hopefully she'll pass out at home and sleep it off."

"I mean do you think she's safe to drive—like *that?*" I ask.

Dad sighs. "Not much we can do about it."

"I could call the police." Larry shuts the door. "They might be able to catch her."

"She'll probably be long gone before they even send a car out." Dad's tone turns matter-of-fact tone. "Why bother?"

"Maybe she'll pass a patrol car on her way," Larry says lightly as he opens the fridge. "That'd be fun to see. Think she'd swear at a cop like that?" He hands my dad a beer. "I think we deserve this."

Suddenly they're joking about the whole thing, and I can't help but feel sorry for my mom. It seems cruel to laugh at her expense. Like making fun of a handicapped child or kicking a stray dog. Yet I know it's pointless to defend her. Really, she doesn't deserve it. And, despite their insensitivity, there's no way I'm going home tonight. My mom would probably kill me.

Sixteen

IT WAS NEARLY MIDNIGHT WHEN MOIRA woke up on the living room floor. She didn't remember how she'd gotten there, but since she was fully dressed, she assumed it must've occurred during the daytime. Seeing her car keys on the floor nearby, she wondered if she'd been about to go somewhere. But then she noticed her purse and its contents spilled out in the foyer. Had she already been somewhere?

She stooped down to scoop up the contents, trying to remember. And slowly, as she made her way to her bedroom, it came back to her in fragmented pieces. She'd gone to Larry's to get Kiera. But had Kiera come home? Somehow she didn't think so. And why did she want to get her?

Moira went into the bathroom and, blinking at the

overly bright lights, she stared into the mirror. Who was that horrid looking woman? She reached up to touch her face then, cringing, turned away. What was happening to her? She saw the box of booze on the bathroom floor, right where she'd set it after her trip to the liquor store, where she'd told the clerk they were having a big party. She hadn't mentioned it was a party of one.

Now she remembered what had derailed her. When she'd opened her prescription of Tylenol 3—because she'd felt a headache coming on—she'd been shocked to see there were only four pills there. Four pills! How could that be? So she'd opened another prescription to see it only had five pills! Her precious prescriptions—that she'd worked so hard to acquire last week—had all been pilfered from. And she knew this was the work of her middle child. But upon tearing through the house and screaming Kiera's name, she eventually concluded that Kiera was gone. Her bike was gone too. Then Moira had seen Kiera's snotty little text message. After reading it several times, she felt certain her daughter was guilty.

Out of pure frustration, Moira popped a couple pills, downing them with a tumbler of vodka. Then she tried to call Kiera. When Kiera didn't answer, Moira left a somewhat controlled message, followed up by several irate text messages. When she never heard from her bratty daughter, Moira had decided to do something about it.

"Oh, God!" Moira groaned loudly. She didn't approve of taking the Lord's name in vain, but perhaps this was a prayer—a prayer of utter desperation. Had she really gone to Larry's house and created a horrible scene—or was she simply delusional? As angry as she still felt toward Kiera, she hated the idea of losing control in front of Larry and Alex and God only knew who else. How humiliating.

Moira looked at her reflection again, forcing herself to take in the ugliness. Was this what she'd become—in just a short time? What would she be like a month from now? No wonder her family had left her. Isn't that what Kiera had said this morning? That they'd all left her—because she was such a horrible person. Moira opened up the prescription bottles, pouring out the contents of all of them into the palm of her hand… and staring at them. Different shapes and colors… All combined they were probably enough to end her pain, once and for all. Especially if she topped them off with plenty of alcohol.

She picked up an unopened bottle of vodka and, with the pills still in her hand, went upstairs. Into Hannah's room. She turned on the light, comforted to see that everything in here was the same as always, never changing. The only place Moira could ever find peace—even if just a sliver. She sat down in the wicker rocker that Hannah had painted pale blue, on the soft cushion that Hannah had sewn a patchwork cover for, and let out a long, tired sigh. "Oh, Hannah," she said quietly. "Why did you have to go like that?"

Moira looked around the room, like she often did when she was feeling down and low, taking in all the sweet touches that Hannah had so carefully arranged, finally stopping at a photo of the three Josephson girls. Moira had shot the photo, but Hannah had edited it on her computer to look vintage. She'd transformed it into a soft black and white, tinted with pastels. Moira had taken it on Easter morning—about six years ago. Back when all three girls didn't mind getting dressed up for church. Standing on the front porch, holding their Easter baskets, with smiles as pure as sunshine. Hannah, as usual, had looked almost angelic. But Kiera with her long brown hair and serious dark eyes looked sweet and innocent. And little Maddie—so hopeful and happy, as if her life couldn't get any better. And maybe it couldn't.

Moira stared at Maddie—her baby—knowing that she was about to fail her. Just like she had failed Kiera. But Kiera was nearly grown and tougher than any of them. Little Maddie, though. She was still so young and vulnerable. What would it do to her, to lose her sister and mother within six months of each other? Moira looked at the pills in her hand. *Just flush them,* she told herself. *Stop this madness.*

She went back downstairs and stood by the toilet, ready to dump the pills...but couldn't. Instead she poured them back into one of the pill bottles and hid it in her lingerie drawer, beneath a padded bra. Just in case. And telling herself she was done with the pills, she poured herself a tumbler of vodka and chugged it down. One step at a time… Isn't that what they taught in twelve step programs?

I awake to the sound of muted male whispers. Opening one eye, I can see the shadowy outlines of Larry and Dad in the kitchen. I roll over on the great room couch and, pulling the blanket over my head, pretend to be asleep. Dad mentioned an early morning tee-time last night, but it's not even light outside. What was wrong with these guys? Hadn't they just played eighteen holes yesterday? Well, fine—but I am sleeping in!

I listen to them leave, but now I'm wide awake. And hungry. I forage around the kitchen, finally deciding on a Yoplait yogurt and piece of toast smothered in butter. I've barely given up being vegan and now I'm obsessed with dairy. Maybe my body has missed the calcium. Whatever.

I straighten up my borrowed sleeping area then putter around for a while, watching CNN and then the Weather Channel until I'm bored and restless. To amuse myself, I wander around the house—exploring. AKA snooping. But seeing Larry's kids' rooms, all three of whom are still in grade school, is depressing. It reminds me of the old days—back when our family was happy.

Finally it's around nine and I have to get out of here. It's like I can't breathe or am about to scream. So I leave my hosts a thank you note, written on a paper towel, and hop on my bike. It's still cool out and, not particularly wanting to go home—and face Mom—I decide to take a little bike tour through town. Being that it's Sunday, the streets are quiet and traffic is light.

As I ride down the street where St. Mark's Episcopal Church is located, I slow down. I've always loved this majestic old stone building. From its stately bell towers to arched stained glass windows, it's so gothic and beautiful. And I feel sad to think I've never been inside. As a little girl, I begged my parents to go there, but they just laughed, saying, "That's not our church." My parents' church was a stodgy, boxlike brick building with no personality. And in my opinion, it wasn't much different inside either.

I slow down to admire the old edifice, watching as a few people meet on the stone steps and trickle inside. I'm tempted to park my bike and join them, but I doubt my cutoffs and tank-top are appropriate for such an elegant looking building. Maybe someday. I continue on, riding alongside the rear parking lot, which is about half full. I'm nearly past, but I can't help but put on the brakes to see a very familiar looking old pickup. Unless I'm mistaken, that's Bernard's truck. Rather, his dad's. Do they belong to this church? Interesting.

I continue to ride through town, but with the sun rising higher in the sky, the air's getting warm fast. And so I turn toward home. Hopefully Mom will still be asleep and I can slip in unnoticed. I stop riding in front of my house, but a wave of sadness washes over me as I walk my bike up the driveway. I can't even wrap my head around where it came from. Probably just a combination of everything that's messed up in my life.

And yet it's something more. I feel really detached, like I don't belong anywhere...or to anyone. Like an unmanned boat floating out on the ocean. No direction. No destination. Nothing to be part of. Nothing to hold onto. No one who particularly cares about me. As I go in the house, trying to be stealthy, I have the sensation that if I were to vanish from the face of the earth right here and right now, no one would probably notice...or care too much. Not for a while anyway. I try to brush it away, but the chilling feel of it seems to cling to me as I tiptoe through the kitchen.

I see no sign of Mom, but her car is in the garage, so I'm sure she's here. But there are no dirty dishes in the sink. Nothing particularly out of place. And with the blinds still down, I suspect she's still sleeping. I take my backpack up to my room but don't really feel like holing up in here all day. And so I decide to pay a visit to the tree house. As painful as it is to read Hannah's diary, I feel compelled to continue with it. I creep back downstairs, grab a few provisions from the kitchen, then head off to my secret hideaway. If only it had AC.

Fortunately, it's not too hot up here yet, and the green leafy shade of the maple tree has a cooling element to it. At least for now. The Altoids tin is still under the window sill, reminding me that my mom might still be plotting my demise—but I don't care to think about that now. Instead, I extract Hannah's diary, find where I left off last time, and continue to read about how hurt and alone and depressed she was in the spring of her junior year. I guess it's true that misery loves company, because, the more I read, the more I can feel Hannah right here with me...like we are crying on each other's shoulders.

Okay, it seems wrong to derive comfort from my dead sister's pain and disappointment. And I do feel bad for her. I'm sorry that she went through all that—and kept it to herself. But it makes me feel oddly connected to her too. And after that chilling sense of disconnection earlier, well, it's something to hold onto. I love that she was writing every day—pouring out her pain on page after page after page. Deliciously sad and hopeless.

But then there's a gap in early April. Hannah doesn't write for more than two weeks, starting in again in mid-April. But her next entry, to my surprise, is shockingly different. So much so that I sort of resent it. To my dismay, Hannah sounds happy.

I can hardly believe it. Just when I felt like I was at the end of myself, ready to give up on everything—the King of the Universe throws me a lifeline. I'm so happy that I feel like singing and dancing. It's like going from pitch-black darkness to a warm glowing light. Like being starved and thirsty and sitting down to a delicious meal—surrounded by loved ones. I really can barely believe it. So much so that I was determined not to write about this experience for two whole weeks. Just in case it wasn't real. But I know it's real. I'm even happier now than I was when it happened.

A couple weeks ago, Wyatt invited—no insisted—that I go on a weekend youth group retreat. But not our church's youth group, which is pretty small and somewhat dull. He asked me to go on a Young Life retreat. After I broke up with him, Wyatt started getting involved in Young Life. And I thought he was probably going off the deep end. But different strokes...

Anyway, Wyatt kept pestering me and even paid my way to go—and, okay, I realize I'm shallow and selfish, but I resented Haley's attempts to win over Wyatt, so I agreed. My sole purpose: to thwart my ex-best friend. And, man, was she ticked to hear I was going. Especially since she wasn't.

The retreat was crazy-fun and not like any of the youth retreats I'd ever been on with my church. But the part that really got to me was when the main speaker talked about what Jesus did on the cross—and why he did it. I suppose I thought I already knew that stuff. I mean I was practically raised in church, right? But what I heard that night about how much God loves me—so much that he would do anything to have an intimate daily friendship with me—I was dumbfounded.

That didn't sound like the God my church taught me about—a God with lots of rules, who scowled down on the rule-breakers and smiled on the obedient. Like I thought I was.

But the God I heard about that night was loving and kind and forgiving—and more than anything wanted me for a friend. That was why he poured himself into Jesus and became man. In order to connect with me—and everyone—so that we could be reunited with a merciful God. It was pretty refreshing, but I still had my doubts. Just the same, when the speaker invited us to make a commitment, I went ahead and did it. I honestly didn't think it was any big deal at the time. But later on, I began to feel this deep sense of something I couldn't even describe. I'd call it joy, but it's deeper than that. It's more like peace. Like feeling safe and loved and connected to God. I am so happy.

I honestly feel like I was dead—or dying—before. But now I am alive. And happy to be alive. I read over the last few pages in here and couldn't believe how sad and lost I sounded. I'm so thankful that God threw me that lifeline. I plan to hold onto it for the rest of my life. And maybe I will even be able to help others to find it too. Woo-hoo! I'm a whole new girl. And it feels just awesome!

I slam the diary down to the tree house floor and swear

loudly. Then, worried that someone might be around to hear me, I just sit there seething inwardly. How could she do this to me? Just when I felt like I understood Hannah, like we were friends again—friends bound together by pain and suffering—and she goes and does that. More than ever, I want to burn this stupid book. I want to forget I ever read those last words. It's just so unfair. So wrong!

I shove the diary down into the hole next to my mom's stupid pills, thinking those two traitors deserve each other. As I whack the loose board back into place, I think maybe I'll bring up matches and set this whole tree house on fire. Because one thing I know for sure, I don't want to read any more of Hannah's dumb diary. I feel tricked and betrayed and incredibly angry. As I march into the house, I think that if Mom says one cross word to me, I will tear her freaking head off. I seriously pity the next person who messes with me.

Seventeen

BY MONDAY MORNING, I'VE COOLED OFF some. Oh, I'm still mad, but at least I have a job to distract myself with. And, quite honestly, I'm looking forward to seeing Bernard again. Plus I'm relieved to hear that our weather is supposed to cool down to the low eighties this week. That sounds doable. As I finish my bowl of cereal and coffee, I'm relieved that Mom's not up yet. She never even spoke to me yesterday. Maybe she knew it would be dangerous. When I saw her shuffling through the kitchen in her bathrobe, I did feel a small tinge of pity for her, but I didn't say anything.

As I ride my bike to work, I imagine what it will feel like to be emancipated. Probably not so different than it does now. Except that I'd have to pay rent somewhere. In fact, I wonder why I should even bother with the legalities of getting my freedom. After all, my mom's pretty much ignoring me now. If this keeps up, why not just live at home, come and go as I please, and save up money for college?

As I lock my bike, Bernard comes over. His smile suggests he's genuinely happy to see me. "Val just called," he says. "She's bringing over some paint for the mural this morning."

"Cool." I follow him inside the park, where several kids are already playing on the playground. As usual, they hop off the swings and slides and rush over to us. They remind me of hungry puppies about to get fed. Sheena and Sicily are among the shuffle, both rushing to me for their morning hugs. I actually love this part of the job. It reminds me of how Maddie used to be, before she got too old for this. They entice me to play hopscotch, and Bernard gets some of the older kids organized for a box hockey tournament.

As the day progresses, I think I'm pretty lucky to have a job that is mostly about playing with kids in the park. Then, when Val arrives with quarts of donated paint in all the colors of the rainbow, I set several of the kids to work. I've already sketched the outline of the picture that we all decided on last week. I'd shown them several rough sketches of scenes that I thought would be fun and easy to paint and for some reason they glommed onto the hot air balloons.

I give them some points and tips, then using old t-shirts

as paint smocks and a couple of stepladders, we start to paint. I don't know what to expect—besides drips and messes—but to my surprise, they work hard to put the paint where it needs to go. By lunchtime, we have almost one whole wall finished. And to my relief, it doesn't look too bad—when you're about twenty feet away from it. I help the kids wash up and tell them we'll get back to it tomorrow morning. My plan is to keep it a morning activity.

As usual, we gather our free lunch sacks then go beneath our favorite shade tree to eat. After lunch, Bernard and I take turns telling the kids tall tales, which is our way of getting everyone to relax for a bit. And then the afternoon activities kick into gear. Bernard gets a soccer game going, and I open up the craft table, where I teach Sheena and Sicily and a few others about leaf printing. Then we take a nature walk around the park collecting different items that we will use to paint and print with.

"How was your weekend?" I ask Sheena as she presses an oak leaf onto paper.

"Grandma Jeannie came to visit," she says as she carefully peels off the leaf. "Ooh, isn't that pretty."

"Very nice," I tell her.

"Grandma Jeannie took us shopping," Sicily tells me. "We even got popsicles."

"Yeah, and these too." Sheena sticks out a foot to show off a neon pink flip-flop.

"I thought those were new." I smile. "Pretty."

Before long, it's nearly four o'clock and I lead my crafters over to the hose to wash up, which results in something of a water fight, but cools us all off. Then I tell them it's time to go, sending them on their ways, and go over to say good-bye to Bernard.

"This looks great," he tells me as he locks the supply shed. "I can't believe the kids did such a good job. I was expecting it to look more like modern art."

"I know." I smile. "But they were really into staying in the lines." I explain how I plan to help the wobbly places by going around the whole thing with black outlines when we're done.

"Cool." He nods toward his pickup. "Want a ride?"

I actually do want a ride but hate to look too eager... or pathetic.

"Come on," he urges, "I know you do."

"Only if you let me treat you to a Slurpee," I say.

"Deal." He grins. "What're we waiting for?"

Before long, we're back at the sticky white plastic table next to 7-Eleven, wearing our Ranger Rick suits and sipping on Slurpees like a couple of nerds. Not that I mind.

"How are you doing?" he asks with what seems a concerned look.

"Doing?" I act oblivious, as if I haven't told him most of our family secrets.

"You know, with your mom and everything. How'd it go?"

I give him the quick lowdown. "I guess it could be worse."

"I guess." He nods. "And it might get better too."

"I'm not so sure about that." I study him closely. "Can I ask you a personal question?"

His brows arch above his dark rimmed glasses. "Yeah, sure."

"Do you go to church? I mean to St. Mark's? I thought I saw your pickup—I mean your dad's pickup—there on Sunday."

"Were you there?" He looks surprised.

"No. Just riding by on my bike. I paused to look at that church. I always thought it was so pretty. And it looked like your pickup. Made me curious."

"As a matter of fact, I was there on Sunday." He looks slightly sheepish. "I haven't been there for a while. Not since I went to college last fall. But it was my mom's church."

"Oh."

"My Dad would probably prefer if I didn't go there."

"Why?"

"Because he's Jewish. Not that he goes to temple regularly. But he hoped I'd follow in that tradition."

"And you didn't?"

"I actually like both. So did my mom. When she was alive, we took turns. Church one weekend and temple the next. It was pretty cool, really."

"Sounds interesting." I frown as I play with my straw, squeaking it against the plastic lid. "So, do you believe in God?"

"Sure." He nods. "How about you?"

I shrug.

"Let me guess. It kind of goes with being vegan…are you an atheist?"

I shrug again but don't remind him that I gave up on the vegan thing.

"That must be hard for you, Kiera. I mean, in light of your sister's death."

"So are you saying I should believe in God just because my sister died?"

"No, of course not."

"Is that why you do? Because your mom died?"

"No, that's not why. Although it's a comfort. But I believe in God because it makes more sense than not believing in him."

"Really?" I narrow my eyes. "How's that?"

"Just look around." He chuckles as I stare at the Dumpster. "Well, not here. But look around at nature. Look at the mountains or the ocean or a hummingbird or the millions of stars out there…It all seems to suggest that there's a creator."

"So you believe that old fable about God creating the world in seven days?" I challenge him, ready to debate over evolution.

But he just laughs. "I don't know about that. But I do believe it took a lot of thinking and planning and creativity to create this planet. I can't even wrap my head around the universe. It's too miraculous—I don't think we can understand the massiveness of creation with a human brain. I guess that's where faith comes in. At least, that's how my mom used to explain it to me."

I don't respond to this but simply let his words roll through my head, like the dryer on fluff cycle, going round and round. I might not agree, but it's an interesting way to look at it.

"So are you an atheist?" He removes his lid and drinks down the last of his Slurpee.

"That's what I used to tell my sister." I frown to remember the last entry in her diary. It's starting to make sense now. The way she became more outspoken about her faith that last year of her life. I had imagined she'd always been like that, but the truth was she'd simply been a good girl, not a fanatic.

"Why did you tell your sister that?" he probes.

"Probably to irritate her," I confess.

"You didn't really mean it?"

"I'm not sure. I mean, an atheist denies God's existence. And like Hannah used to tell me, it takes more faith to be an atheist than a believer."

"You mean in case you're wrong?"

I just nod.

"Better to hedge your bets?"

"Maybe. But I guess I'm really more of an agnostic. Maybe there is a God. But I don't think he's too interested in me. And I'm not too interested in him." Okay, that's a lie. I think I *am* interested. But just too proud to admit it.

He tosses his cup into the trash and leans back, folding his arms behind his head without saying anything.

I noisily slurp up the last of my drink then look evenly at him. "So…do you think less of me now?"

He sits up straight with a startled look. "No, of course not."

"Oh, I thought maybe you were judging me."

He slowly shakes his head. "Not at all. I think it's cool that you're on your own spiritual journey, Kiera. Some people don't even give God a second thought. I think that's pretty shortsighted. I like that you're willing to have a conversation about it. I have no doubt you'll figure it out."

I toss my cup into the trash and stand, wishing I was as confident as Bernard, but at the same time grateful that he hasn't turned his nose up at me for my lack of faith. That's something. "You know," I say quietly. "I've always wanted to peek inside of your church. I mean at St. Mark's. It's so beautiful from the outside. I'd like to see the inside. You know, from an artistic point of view."

"Why don't you go there with me next Sunday?" he suggests.

"You mean to a whole service?"

"Sure, why not?"

"I'll think about it," I promise as we walk back to his pickup. And, even though I'm pretty sure I'd like to go there with him, I don't want to lay it out like that. Don't want to appear too eager—or like I think he's making a date with me. That would be stupid.

We talk about work and the kids and the plans we have for the upcoming week as he drives me home. I'm surprised with all the ideas he comes up with for the kids, and when I ask him about it, he confesses that he's been doing some studying.

"I found some old Boy Scout books in my grandma's attic that are pretty interesting. Then I did some online searching." He pulls into my driveway. "I want to make sure we keep those kids busy with something good this summer."

"Cool." I glance curiously at him as he helps me unload my bike in my driveway. Bernard is not your typical guy. Not at all. But just because he's not doesn't mean I have to fall for him. Besides that, he's probably just being nice to me. The same way he's nice to all the kids at the park. "Thanks for the ride," I say lightly as I push the remote door opener that I keep in my bike basket. "See you tomorrow." But as I wheel my bike into the garage, I feel unexpectedly sad to part ways with him. And I wish that we could be more than just friends.

"Who's that?" My mom asks in a sharp tone as I park my bike in its usual spot.

I'm surprised to see her standing on the step by the backdoor, but I act nonchalant. Like she always greets me this way. "Just a coworker," I say as I push the remote to lower the door, watching as it goes down, like it's riveting.

"He's a waiter?" she says as I walk past her.

"A waiter?" I peer curiously at her. Although she's dressed today, it's just sweats and pretty sloppy looking, for her. "Huh?"

"Yeah. Don't you work at the Outback?"

"What?" I cock my head to one side. Seriously, is she losing it?

"That uniform." She points down at me.

Okay, I can't help but chuckle as I go inside. Talk about checked out. "Is that where you think I've been working?" I ask when we're both in the kitchen.

"Well, isn't it?"

I hide my amusement as I open the fridge, which looks pretty stark. Mom obviously hasn't gotten groceries lately. Guess I'll have to use that money Dad gave me and do it myself. I take an apple that looks a little dicey then turn to see her still staring at me with a confused expression. Does she honestly think I've been working at a restaurant? "As a matter of fact, I'm employed by Parks and Rec. I'm a park counselor at Greenwood Park."

She wrinkles her nose. "Greenwood's a bad part of town. Some pretty rough people live over there."

"Depends on your perspective. The kids are awfully sweet. But some of the parents, similar to ones in nicer neighborhoods, could use some help." As I walk away I wonder if she even gets it. But I don't stick around to find out. I'm still a little worried that she's going to lay into me over her missing pills. As I hurry up the stairs, I wonder if she's still using them. She certainly had enough to keep her going for a while. Well, depending on how many she takes. Or more than likely, she's figured out new ways to get them. For all I know she could be buying them off the street, maybe from some of the "rough people" who live in Greenwood.

Whatever the case, I'm determined to stay out of it from now on.

Eighteen

SUMMER NIGHTS CAN BE PAINFULLY LONG...
and unbearably lonely. Especially on a Friday night when
it seems like everyone else is out having fun. Not for the
first time I wonder what is wrong with me. And how can
I fix it? Maybe it's hopeless.

As I take refuge in the tree house, gloomily watching
the leafy shadows in the oncoming sunset, I feel more
than just hopeless. I feel seriously angry. I toss my dead
sister's diary to the floor, swearing to never read another
page of her blissful drivel. After reading about ten entries,
I'm thoroughly disgusted. Not only is Hannah still delir-
iously happy in her newfound faith—she's agreed to go
to prom with Wyatt. But only if they maintain a "pure relationship." Of course, he's in agreement, and to be fair,
that's not what aggravates me the most.

It's simply the fact that she sounds so freaking happy. She's even forgiven Haley for being such a fair-weather friend—back when Hannah needed her most. And thanks to Hannah, Haley has "found real faith too" and they're BFFs again. Haley even claims to be glad that Hannah and Wyatt are back together. Like everything is just peachy keen and coming up roses. Nauseating. I actually had to go back and read a few of Hannah's darker entries, where she's stressed and depressed, just to convince myself that she had actually been nearly suicidal. And, okay, so I didn't imagine her misery…but how did she bounce back so quickly? Although things always did come easily to my older sister.

The upside of this new happy Hannah is knowing that she probably didn't intentionally run into that tree last New Year's Eve. The downside is that makes me feel truly guilty for her death. But I refuse to dwell on that now. Instead, I'm thinking about how miserable it feels not to have a single friend. Normally, it's not something I care to think about. Except that I feel so isolated and alone right now. A pathetic loser hiding up here in my little tree house while everyone else is out enjoying a nice summer evening.

And since I'm already so miserable, I allow myself to revisit the past. I start with the previous summer, because that seems like the last time my life was somewhat normal. As usual, I spent as much time as possible with my two besties. Lana and Meg and I had been like the three musketeers since middle school, and we were having so much fun that we didn't want summer to end.

Then school started and my life went completely sideways, thanks to a love triangle involving Meg and me and our mutual crush Tyler Gregg. When Meg won—by default—and Lana took Meg's side, I was immediately odd girl out—and I didn't take it very well. As a result, they both shunned me like I had a contagious disease.

I was so hurt I didn't know what to do. And that's when I started my tough girl act. I quit caring about my appearance and refused to go out for sports. If Mom would've let me, I'd probably have accumulated a bunch of tattoos by now. As it turns out, I'm glad I didn't. Tats are getting to be so common these days. But my response to my friends' betrayal was to go under. To occupy myself, I turned to my music and art—and pushed everyone else, including my family, away.

It seemed a good defense at the time. I hadn't planned to keep it up indefinitely. In fact, during winter break, I attempted to make amends with Lana and Meg. I even went to the sleepover at Lana's that night, on New Year's Eve. How I wish I hadn't!

Then Hannah died and, as they say, the die was cast. So here I am, alone and sad. The closest thing I have to a friend these days is Bernard. And I'm pretty sure he's only nice to me because we work together—and because he has a big heart and is sorry for me. But all week, it was just work as usual. He gave me a couple rides home early in the week. But then he got his little car back and I was on my own. I hoped he'd drive the pickup today, but he didn't. And he never said another word about going to church with him. I suppose I'd acted too nonchalant when he asked me. Or maybe he just forgot.

As I struggle to keep from drowning in my cesspool of self-pity, I notice a car slow down on our street. It catches my eye because it's a flashy yellow color, and I haven't noticed it in our neighborhood before. I wonder if it's pulling into our driveway, but then it parks. It's on our side of the street, but across from the Baxter house. Curious, I watch as the driver's door opens and the interior light reveals a guy with bushy blond hair. He's looking down at his phone. Then he gets out and I can see he's tall and built—like a football player. And, if I'm not mistaken, he looks a whole lot like Maxwell Harter. So much so that an interior alarm goes off inside of me. Seriously, is that Max out there? And, if so, why?

As Max crosses the street, I drop the rope ladder and scramble down, scurrying over to the hedge alongside our property, where I crouch in the shadows to watch. The big guy ambles up to the front of the house where the porch light illuminates him even better, and I am certain it's Max. Then Nora comes out the front door, embraces him, and they get into his shiny car and take off.

I am seriously dumbfounded. Maxwell Harter is dating Nasty Nora? Okay, she's not really nasty, and I probably should let that title go. But as I continue to crouch by the hedge, I wonder. Does Nora *know* who she's dating? What he's really like? What if Max does to her what he did to Hannah? I can't just stand by and watch it happen. But what can I do? I consider texting Nora a warning, but that's too obvious and traceable. I consider the desktop computer and printer in the den, but there's the slight chance my mom might crawl out of her room and question me. Although that seems unlikely since she's been holed up there all week. She doesn't go to work, and if I hadn't gotten groceries yesterday, there wouldn't even be any food in the house. I don't know if she's drunk or high or what, but I do know she's not going to work anymore.

But back to my dilemma. I consider a simple hand-written note to Nora. Maybe I could pretend it came from Hannah—beyond the grave. But that doesn't seem terribly smart. Besides, handwriting is so identifiable. As I'm going into the house, I remember something I saw in an old suspense movie. And before long, I'm in my room, wearing a pair of winter gloves to conceal any fingerprints, and cutting letters from an old magazine. I glue the pieces onto a paper to spell out this message:

NORA
MAX IS A RAPIST
BE CAREFUL

I paste the letters of her name onto an envelope, put it all together and then, really caught up in the suspense

element, and concerned that the Baxters might have a security cam somewhere, I dress in black jeans and black
hoodie and, still wearing my gloves, pull up the hood and
sneak back outside. I jog a few houses down, to conceal
my direction, just in case, then stealthily go by the Baxters', slipping my letter into their mailbox before taking
another route back home. Success!

I feel slightly breathless—and excited—as I go back to
my tree house, thinking I'll watch until they come back—
and then I get another idea. Okay, I'll admit it's not a well
thought out plan, but I'm in such a state that I don't really
care. This might be because, even though I haven't finished reading Hannah's diary, I feel certain she won't do
anything to bring justice to Max. I know she never went
to the authorities, not when it happened or even later. I'm
sure I would've heard about it if she had. And it's just so
wrong for him to get away with it. And to possibly do it
again. For all I know, he could be a serial rapist—with
other girls remaining silent. And so I decide to take the
law into my own hands. I will execute this new diabolical
plan.

I get my artists supplies box from my room, along with
a can of black spray paint from the garage, and head up to
the tree house, where by the light of the flashlight, I hand
cut a stencil from mat board—with six capital letters that
say: RAPIST. Then I take my stencil and paint, along with
my gloves, and go hide in the shadows of the hedge. As I
wait there, I feel slightly giddy—or just nervous. Accord-

ing to my phone it's nearly midnight. But Nora's a graduate, maybe she doesn't have a curfew. Or maybe they came back while I was in the house. Maybe I'm being a complete idiot.

But then I see headlights and, as the car slows down, I know it's Max's. He's coming the same direction as before, and it looks like he's about to park in the same place. I'm tempted to shake my spray can again but don't want anyone to hear it. Besides, I've already shaken it hard. The question is, will Max get out of the car and walk Nora to the house? Being that he's such a jerk, it seems unlikely. But then he does. And now I have my chance—staying low, armed with stencil and paint, I scurry over to his car.

My hands shake as I hold my stencil against the trunk and then I spray, waving it back and forth several times before I make a run, alongside the hedge and through the shadows, back to the tree house. I can't believe what I've just done. As I peer from my perch, it's too dark to see if the word even shows up, and then just like that, Max is back in his car and driving away.

Feeling like a criminal—and I guess I am—I take all evidence of my crime back into the house. I burn the stencil materials and my gloves, as well as the magazine I chopped up, in the family room fireplace in the basement. I even have a story prepared for Mom just in case she comes down here, but she doesn't. I make sure it burns until nothing remains but black ashes, which I stir up some. Then I wrap the spray-paint can in newspaper and shove it into the garbage can, burying it deep. The garbage doesn't go out until Monday, but I'll make sure the can is on the street.

Then, still feeling like a criminal, I go and take a nice long shower. I tell myself it's because I never took one after work, but I know that it's more than that. I want to wash away the traces of guilt still clinging to me. But as I get ready for bed, I rationalize my delinquent behavior. Max deserved it. And, really, he deserves much, much worse. But there's only so much a girl can do. Hopefully this won't all come back to bite me. And maybe I don't care. After all, if Max wants to make a fuss, I'd be glad to confess to anyone—to everyone—why I did what I did. Even if it means time in jail. Bring it!

I spend most of Saturday at Larry's house on the pretense of wanting to be with Dad, but the truth is I don't want to be home in case the police—or Max Harter—come after me. I realize I'm probably just suffering from irrational paranoia, but just the same, I don't want to be home. As usual, Dad and Larry go play golf. And, although I consider texting a swim invitation to Bernard, I don't. Call me old fashioned, but I really don't want to look like I'm chasing after a guy. After all, he's just a friend. A friend who appears to have forgotten he promised to take me to church on Sunday.

That evening, when I'm finally feeling more relaxed

about last night's criminal activities, I decide to go home. But when I tell Dad, he objects. "You can't ride your bike home in the dark, Kiera."

"It's not *that* dark," I point out. "And it's not that far."

"You don't even have a bike light," he protests as I get my backpack. "Why don't I just drive you home?"

"Because I need my bike tomorrow."

"Why?"

"So I can go to church." I figure this is a pretty rock-solid argument that should shut him up. Parents should want their kids to go to church.

"If you had your driver's license I'd let you use my car to go home. Then you could drive it to church and drop it by here afterward." He frowns. "Why don't you have your license by now, Kiera? You got your permit on your fifteenth birthday and pestered me nonstop to teach you to drive."

"So?" I suppress aggravation as I shove my stuff into my backpack. Why is Dad being such a freak about this?

"You'll be seventeen this fall. You should have your license by now. Just think, you could drive yourself to school and—"

"Maybe I don't want to drive." I try to conceal my anger. Dad knows I lost interest in driving when I became concerned about fossil fuels and global warming. And then Hannah died...and my resolve turned more than just environmental. I just glare at him. Why is he being so clueless?

"I know, I know." He runs his fingers through his hair. "But you have to get over this paranoia, Kiera. It's not normal. Your fears are ridiculous. You can't go through your whole life not knowing how to drive."

"I don't see why not." I shift my backpack to my other hand. "I gotta go, Dad." He follows me as I head for the door.

"But you never told me about your mom," he says as I unlock my bike. "I sort of hate to ask, but I probably should. How's she doing?"

I shrug. "I haven't really talked to her much." I shove my bike lock into my pack.

"Is she any better? Or worse?"

"I honestly don't know how she is."

"You must have some idea. Don't be so stubborn."

"Well, I know she's not going to work. And she doesn't get groceries. And she looks like a wreck."

Dad grimly shakes his head. "So she's probably still drinking and popping her pills...."

"I really don't know—and I'm trying not to care." I nod to the darkening sky. "I better go or it really will be dark."

Dad gives me a quick hug, telling me to be safe, then I take off. As I ride home, I wonder if this is how my life will always be...bouncing from one house to the next but never feeling at home. I know Dad will only be at Larry's another week or so and then he plans to get a room downtown. I asked him about getting an apartment—something with a spare room that I could use—but he said he wasn't ready for that. I'm not sure if that meant he wasn't ready to commit to an apartment because he's thinking about coming home, or that he doesn't want a spare room because he doesn't want me to live with him. And I was afraid to ask.

Nineteen

ON SUNDAY MORNING, AS I GET READY FOR church, I'm still feeling nervous about vandalizing Max's fancy car. What if someone's security cam caught the whole thing? For all I know, our own security cams could seal my fate, if anyone thinks to check them. And, as crazy as it sounds, I imagine that my going to church this morning might help my case. Might make me look like a nice law-abiding citizen who simply wanted to rectify a wrong done to her poor dead sister. Seriously, what kind of court wouldn't understand this?

Still, as I'm getting out my bike, I find myself looking over my shoulder. I try not to stare at the Baxter house. I'm sure Nora's gotten her letter by now. I almost wish I'd stayed home last night—just in case she went out with Max again. But it felt safer to be gone. I'm rolling my bike out the driveway, wondering how long it will take for me to stop worrying about this and wishing I'd never done it, when I notice Bernard's car pulling up.

He waves then gets out. "Hey, I thought you were going to church with me."

"Oh, yeah." I nod like I just remembered. "I'm sorry."

"Do you have someplace else you need to be?" He points to my bike.

"No, not really. I'll just put this away." As I put my bike back, I can't believe he actually remembered and wanted to make good on his promise. I feel bad that I was thinking the worst of him.

"You look nice." Bernard actually opens the car door for me, like this is a date. Is it? Anyway, I'm glad that I wore my good jeans and a clean t-shirt.

"Thanks," I mutter as I get inside.

After he's in the car, I confess that I was actually going to ride my bike to his church. "I thought you forgot," I tell him.

"That's my fault," he says as he backs out. "I should've let you know. But I was helping my dad yesterday. Had to drive to Tacoma and get a delivery that got waylaid. Didn't get home until late last night."

I lean back and, taking a deep breath, feel myself calming down. It feels like the first time I've relaxed since Friday night. I can't explain it, but for some reason I feel safe with Bernard. As he tells me about his long day of driving yesterday, I decide that I'm not cut out for a life of crime.

I might pretend to be tough, but underneath it all, I'm just a wimp.

As we go into his church, I try to take it all in. It's so big and beautiful and grand. The high ceilings, ornate wood carving, and those glorious stained glass windows. It seems silly—and I blame it on my recent fear of incarceration—but it makes me want to cry. Of course, it's nothing like the church that I grew up in. In this church, everyone stands up and sits down simultaneously—again and again. They read through a little book and recite the same prayer and sing old fashioned hymns. And, if I were into church and God per se, I think I would like this. But, I can't lie to myself, I am mostly here for the architecture. And for Bernard. After the service ends, Bernard leads me over to a classy looking woman with shoulder length silver hair. Her eyes light up when she sees him, and I soon learn she's his grandmother. He introduces me, and she warmly grasps my hand, welcoming me to church. I can tell by the way she glances back at Bernard that she's assuming I'm his girlfriend...and I find myself wishing it were true.

"How did you like it?" he asks as we get back into his car.

"Like it?" I'm still stuck on the idea of being his girlfriend.

"Church."

"Oh, the building is fabulous." I return to reality. "And the service, well, it was different. I like it better than the church I used to go to with my family. But that's about it. I mean, despite those beautiful windows, I didn't feel like God peeled back that gorgeous high ceiling to personally speak to me. Sorry."

Bernard just laughs.

"Your grandmother seems sweet."

"She really is. Although I'm afraid she's jumping to conclusions."

"Conclusions?"

"About you. She thinks we're dating. But I'll straighten her out."

"Oh, yeah. Good." I feel my cheeks warming as the cartoon dream cloud above my head goes "Poof!"

"My mom and I used to go out for pancakes after church. You interested?"

"Are you kidding?" I pat my midsection. "Did you hear my stomach rumble during that baby dedication?"

He chuckles. "So that was you. I thought it was me."

After we're seated at Lou's Pancake House, a place I've never been but always wanted to go, Bernard asks how I'm doing. He does it in such a way that assures me he really cares and doesn't want some pat answer.

"To be honest, I'm feeling pretty nervous," I admit. "I did something kind of stupid the other night. I mean, it seemed cool at the time...but then I kind of regretted it."

He grimaces. "Something with your mom again?"

"No, nothing new there. Although she did get a deadbolt installed on her bedroom door, but I'm not taking it personally." I fidget with my napkin, trying to decide how much to say or if I should just keep my mouth shut, but because the waiter comes I get a chance to gather my thoughts as I order blueberry pancakes and coffee.

"So now you've got me really curious," he says after the waiter goes. "What did you do that you regret?"

I look directly into his dark brown eyes. "Can I trust you?"

He nods with a sincere expression. "Of course."

"It's a long and sort of involved story," I say slowly. "But I really need to talk to someone about it. If I don't, I'm afraid I might explode...or implode...or something. But it won't be pretty."

"Go for it, Kiera. You can trust me."

"Well, it involves my sister Hannah's story—and another embarrassing confession." So I tell him about stealing Hannah's diary and how I've been slowly reading it. "At first it just helped me to feel connected to her. Then something happened to her. Something pretty bad. And she never told anyone about it." I pause as the waiter sets down our orders, wondering if I can possibly tell this story and eat at the same time. After he leaves, I look at Bernard. "Maybe I can finish telling you later. I mean, it's kind of emotional. I'd hate to cry on my pancakes."

"Yeah, sure. Might make them soggy."

And so, while we're eating, Bernard does a great job of carrying the conversation. He tells me about how he and his mom used to come here. "We did a lot together. Dad worked so much, and I'm an only child. So Mom and I hung out a lot." He tells me about how his mom took him on vacations too. "We went to Yosemite and Yellowstone. Then, our last trip, right after she was diagnosed, was to the Grand Canyon." He shakes his head. "That was pretty awesome."

"I've never been there," I tell him. "What was your favorite part?"

"We spent the night in the old lodge there. And we got up early in the morning because Mom wanted to see the sunrise. It was pretty cold, but we went out on the rim and watched." He blows out a long sigh. "It was so amazing." He points to me. "You know how beautiful you thought our church windows were this morning?"

"Yeah."

"Well, multiply that by about a million and you'd have the Grand Canyon." He sets down his fork, pushing his empty plate aside.

"Wow, that must've been amazing."

"It was one of those things I mentioned the other day. Sights in nature that make me believe in God. Things that make me know beyond any shadow of doubt that there's a creator. That morning was like that—on steroids."

As Bernard drives me home, I continue telling him about Hannah's diary. It's not easy, but I tell him about the rape, careful not to mention Max's name. "Hannah tore a bunch of pages out of her diary. And I know she partly blamed herself because she'd been drinking. But it sounded like more than just alcohol. I think he slipped her a roofie or something. But, even with the missing pages, her entries strongly suggest it wasn't a consensual act. And she was so miserable afterward that she considered suicide. And even if he didn't drug her—which I doubt— because of their ages, at the very least it would've been considered statutory rape." I pause to see we're in my driveway now and I wonder if I've said too much. "Maybe I shouldn't be telling you all this," I say quietly.

"No, it's okay. I'm just trying to process it. Are you saying that Hannah never told anyone about it?"

"As far as I know, she kept it a secret. I'm guessing her diary is the only evidence."

"Wow. That's tough. So you haven't told your parents?"

"No way. My mother is already a mess, this might finish her off for good. And Dad, well, he would probably buy a gun and shoot Max."

"Max?"

I let out a long sigh. "I didn't mean to say his name."

"Maxwell Harter by any chance?"

I reluctantly nod. "Which brings me to the rest of my tale." I glance nervously around. "But I'm not sure I can tell you here in the driveway."

"Do you want me to come inside?"

"No," I say quickly. "My mom might hear." I look over to my tree house. "Are you a good climber?"

"Does a monkey like bananas?"

I explain my plan, and the next thing I know we're up in the tree house. "Welcome to my world," I say as I sit down.

"This is cool," he says. "Small, but cool."

"I guess you might as well know all my secrets." I pry up the loose board and remove both the Altoids box and Hannah's diary.

"Hey, I could do with a mint." He reaches for it, but I stop him, explaining the contraband contents. Then I open the diary, finding the section about Max and solemnly hand it to him, waiting nervously while he reads it.

"Man, I bet this could be used in a court of law." He finally says, reverently handing it back.

"I thought of that. But how would Hannah feel? I mean, it's bad enough that I've trespassed into her privacy by reading this. And now I've let you see it. But for the whole world? Wouldn't it be like dragging her name through the mud?" Now I describe how everyone was so kind at her memorial, saying what a fine, good, sweet, kind, angelic girl she was. "And it's true, she was incredibly good. Sometimes I hated her for it. But for her to be remembered by something like this, well, it seems unfair... and unkind."

He slowly nodded. "I see what you mean."

So now I tell him about Max and Nora and what I did on Friday night. His eyes get so big, I'm pretty sure he thinks I should be locked up—probably for insanity.

Strangely enough, I feel slightly better for getting it out. Embarrassed, but better.

"Wow, Kiera, I can't believe you did that."

"I know." I stare down at the Altoid box still in my lap. "And if I think my mom is nuts, I must be certifiable, huh?"

"Well, I don't know. I mean you could really get into trouble. But on the other hand, if Max really did that—and it sure looks like it—then he deserves some serious consequences. And I think it was thoughtful to warn Nora."

I brighten slightly. "And even if Max somehow figured out it was me, and pressed charges, I would confess and explain why I did what I did. Then everyone would know that he's a rapist. There'd be some satisfaction in that."

"Yeah...and then there's that old saying."

"What saying?"

"Two wrongs don't make a right."

I sigh then nod. "I've actually felt pretty guilty about the whole thing."

"I wonder what Max did when he saw the stencil—or how long it took him to notice it."

"I wondered about that too."

Bernard rubbed his chin. "I know where he lives."

"What?"

"It's not far from my house."

"You're kidding."

"Nope. In fact, Max and I used to be pretty good

friends. Back in grade school. By middle school, he turned into a jock and pretty much left me in the dust."

"You were friends with Maxwell Harter?" I can't believe it—they're total opposites.

"We could just happen to casually drive by his house," Bernard said with a mischievous twinkle. "See if his car is there. Get a quick look then keep going."

I'm already stashing the diary and Altoids box beneath the window sill. "What are we waiting for?" I toss down the ladder.

As Bernard drives us to his neighborhood, he makes it clear that he's not condoning what I did. "I understand your motives, Kiera, but it wasn't a smart move. You could be the one who got in trouble with the law. And Max could just walk away."

"Believe me, I know it was stupid. It's just that, at the time, well, I wasn't thinking right." I'm tempted to admit that I'm uber-lonely and have no real friends, but it sounds so pathetic.

"That's his house up ahead. The gray one with black shutters." He slows just a bit.

"That's it," I say quietly. "The yellow car in the driveway."

"Looks pretty new."

As we get closer, I glimpse the rear of his car to see there's a big college bumper sticker covering where I stenciled. But all around the bumper sticker are the tell-tale splatters of black spray-paint. Not pretty.

"Wow." Bernard looks straight forward and I try to do the same. "You really got him good, Kiera. I mean, uh, *bad*."

I resist the urge to slump down in the seat, simply looking ahead with what I hope is an innocent expression... just in case Max is watching. "I didn't know I was so generous with the paint that night. But it was dark. I wanted to be sure the message was clear and easy to read."

"I wonder how long it took for him to figure it out," Bernard says as he continues down the street, turning at the next corner.

"It was pretty late, and I'm guessing he was clueless about it. I'll bet it sat out all night and into the next morning, and however long it took him to get up and notice it."

"Well, he's obviously noticed it. I wonder how many others did too."

"I wish I could've seen his face."

"That's our house." He points to ranch house similar to Max's, except that it's light blue with white shutters. The old pickup is parked in front of it. "Not as fancy as your house."

"Fancy houses are highly overrated," I say.

"Going by Max's reminded me of something."

"What?"

"Back in grade school. Max's parents had problems—that ended in divorce. But I remember how mean Max's dad could be. Both to Max's mom and to Max and his older brother too. Mr. Harter was a real bully."

"Maybe that has something to do with Max being such a jerk. But it's no excuse."

"No, it's not an excuse, but it's an explanation."

"Maybe."

"And I remember something else, Kiera."

"What?" I'm trying not to feel irritated. Is Bernard trying to defend his childhood friend? To make me feel sorry for Max? Because it's pointless.

"Max was really sympathetic to me when my mom was sick."

"Uh-huh."

"I'm not trying to make you feel bad for what you did. Just trying to get you to see that Max isn't the devil. I think what he did to your sister was terrible—and I wish she'd gone to the police. But I don't think it's healthy for you to bear her grudge for her. If the law's not involved, you probably shouldn't be either."

"Well, I'll admit vandalizing his car wasn't too smart," I say. "But I can still hate him. And I do hate him. If murder was legal, I think I could kill him."

Bernard doesn't say anything in response to this.

"And what if he's still doing crud like that?" I demand. "Max Harter could be a serial rapist for all we know."

"I guess so. But, somehow, I don't think so."

"But how would you know? Hannah probably didn't think so either. Look what happened to her. And what about Nora the other night? Who knows what happened?"

"Well, if anything did happen to Nora, I hope she'll report it."

"Hey, do you think that bumper sticker on his car was for his college?" I'm getting a new idea now.

"I heard he got a football scholarship."

"And maybe girls on his campus should be warned about Maxwell Harter."

"Like you did for Nora? You plan to send them all anonymous notes?"

"No, of course, not. But I've heard of websites where you can post information on people—like a warning."

"Wouldn't that be slander?"

"Not if it were true."

We're nearly to my house again when Bernard turns to look at me. "Kiera, how about if we make a deal?"

"What kind of deal?"

"If you'll put this to rest—for a while—I'll look into it myself. I'll play sleuth. I'll try to reconnect with Max and see if I can find out what's up."

"But he might suspect you, Bernard." I suddenly imagine a muscular Max pounding the crud out of Bernard.

"I doubt that. We used to be friends. And we still say hey when we see each other. No big deal."

"I don't want you to be in any danger." Now I wish I'd never told him.

"Yeah, well, maybe that's how I feel about you, Kiera. Maxwell is a big tough guy. And you're just a skinny little girl. What would he have done if he'd caught you vandalizing his car the other night?"

I cringe to imagine. Especially since my disguise probably made me look like a young punk. He might've killed me.

"So, will you make a deal with me?" Bernard parks in my driveway again. "Agree to back off and let me do some snooping?"

I shrug. "I guess it can't hurt. As long as you're careful." I thank him for church and pancakes and then, still feeling uneasy for Bernard's safety, I go inside. I shouldn't have told Bernard this. What if he winds up on Maxwell's radar and simply makes things worse? Why didn't I just keep my stupid nose out of this? Don't I have enough troubles without creating new ones?

Twenty

MOIRA HADN'T BEEN TO WORK IN NEARLY A month. She'd convinced Lisa that she simply needed some downtime. "To process everything." And Lisa had seemed relieved at the time. She'd probably figured it would make it easier in the end, to simply ease Moira out of their office. But Moira had really convinced herself it was just a break. Time for her to get it together.

And yet, here it was July and she was still falling apart. Alex, she'd learned through Kiera, had moved out of Larry's house. But her tightlipped daughter had not revealed where. But at least Alex was still paying the bills. That was something. But how long would it last? What would happen to her when he filed for divorce? And she knew he would. Somehow she had to get it together. And so she'd made an appointment with Lisa—to discuss returning to work.

They agreed to meet at Frisco's Wine Bar at three, a place where fellow realtors liked to meet after work sometimes. Moira hoped they wouldn't be there at that earlier hour. She'd spent most of the day just getting ready for this meeting. And when she looked at herself in the full-length mirror before leaving, she thought she looked like the old Moira Josephson. Or nearly.

Moira had been out of pills for long enough to lose the clawing, burning desire for them. Whoever had stolen them from her—either Kiera or Alex—had probably done her a favor. But she'd still been drinking. And to fortify herself for this meeting, she'd downed a tumbler of vodka then vigorously brushed her teeth and rinsed with minty mouthwash before applying an even coat of frosted pink lipstick.

Lisa was already there when Moira arrived. As usual, she looked chic and confident. Even though Lisa was ten years younger than Moira, she had a more impressive degree, plus more years of real estate experience. And she was the manager of their company. But Lisa had always liked Moira. And when Hannah died, Lisa had been kind and supportive.

They exchanged the usual light embrace and air kisses, then headed for a booth in back. "You look great," Lisa told Moira as she sat down.

"I was about to say the same to you." Moira set her

purse next to her, trying not to notice that her hands were trembling.

"So have you enjoyed your time off?" Lisa asked after they ordered their wine and the small cheese plate.

"I guess so." Moira sighed. "But it wasn't exactly a vacation."

"But good chill time?"

"I think so." Moira pursed her lips. Her goal today was to be somewhat transparent without being brutally honest. "I came to realize that I hadn't really done a good job of processing things...you know, after Hannah's death."

Lisa nodded. "Yes, that's what we all thought."

"I tried to bounce back too soon. Keeping up the façade that I was okay. But I was really in a lot of pain."

Lisa reached over to pat Moira's hand. "That's exactly what I was afraid of."

"But I think I'm better now." Moira sat up straighter, trying to appear more together than she felt. "I think I'm ready to come back to work."

"That'd be wonderful. It's been very busy. And July and August are usually our biggest months. If you don't come back, I'll have to take on a new realtor."

"No, no, I don't want you to do that." Moira paused as their order was set down. Then, as Lisa filled her in on some of the latest listings and sales numbers, Moira reached for her wine. She wanted to sip it slowly, but as Lisa continued to talk, Moira steadily drank it down.

"So, as you can see, we need more hands on deck."

Lisa glanced at the empty glass then continued to chatter about real estate.

"Well, it all sounds good." Moira tried to appear brighter than she felt. "I can't wait to dive in."

"So when will you come back?" Lisa paused as the waiter returned, asking if Moira wanted another glass.

"Thank you." Moira smiled at him then turned to Lisa. "I'd like to come back as soon as possible."

"This week?" Lisa asked with arched brows. "Even though it's almost the Fourth of July, you know how buyers are out house-shopping during holiday weekends. I actually got two sales during the Fourth last year and—"

"I, uh, I'd rather wait and start next week—after the Fourth."

"Oh?" Lisa looked disappointed.

"There's something else you need to know," Moira said solemnly.

"Yes?" Lisa took a dainty sip of wine.

"Alex and I...well, we may be divorcing."

"Oh?" Lisa set her glass down with a startled expression.

"So I really will need a steady income."

"Are you sure? I mean about the divorce—you've been through so much this year. Both of you. Perhaps it's premature to—"

"He's left me, Lisa. He moved out several weeks ago."

"Oh, Moira. I'm so sorry."

"Yes, thanks. It's been rough." Moira felt relieved to see a freshly filled wine glass set before her.

"Are you still seeing your therapist?"

Moira waved a hand. "Not really. She just keeps telling me the same thing."

"What's that?"

"To attend her grief group." Moira sipped her wine.

"Oh, you should do that, Moira. It would be good for you."

"Good to sit in a community center with a bunch of blubbering strangers?" Moira scowled. "That's not my style."

"But if it were helpful?"

"I don't see how." She took a large sip.

"You've got a lot on your plate." Lisa seemed to be studying Moira closely, making her uncomfortable. "Losing a child...divorce. Are you sure you're ready to come back?"

"It's not like I have a choice." Moira felt that old aggravation coming as her defenses let down. "I'll be single soon." She took another sip. "Oh, I know Alex will pay support. For a while anyway. After all, I still have two children at home. But it won't be enough." She laughed, but not with real mirth. "And do you realize that I'll be fifty before long. *Fifty!*" She took a sip, surprised to see her glass was empty again. "I can hardly bear to say that number, but it's true. Fifty is just around the corner."

"You shouldn't obsess on it."

"Don't you understand, Lisa? My best years are behind me."

"Lots of women reinvent themselves at your age." But Lisa's expression told Moira she didn't quite believe it. And why should she? Lisa wasn't even forty yet.

"Alex will probably remarry," Moira continued. "It's nothing for a man his age to remarry. And, of course, it'll be a younger woman." She pointed to Lisa. "Someone like you probably. Pretty, successful, young." She waved her empty glass to the waiter with impatience. What was wrong with him? Didn't he know this was a *wine* bar? Bring on the wine, buddy. Maybe she'd ask him to leave the bottle here next time.

"Do you really think you should have another?" Lisa quietly asked her.

"I absolutely *do* think I should have another," Moira declared.

"How about some of this?" Lisa pushed the cheese plate toward Moira.

Moira grimaced, but took a small piece of white cheese, slowly chewing it as she watched for the waiter to return with her wine.

"Look, Moira, you've been through a lot," Lisa said gently. "And now this news about Alex. Maybe you're not quite ready to come back to work."

"I am ready," Moira declared as the waiter set down a fresh glass of wine. "I *need* to go back to work, Lisa. Can't you see that? It's not doing me any good to stay home—just festering. I need to be out among the living again."

"Well, that might be true, but are you ready to deal with clients again? You know it takes tact, patience, self-control and...*sobriety*."

"I know that." Moira took a big sip, trying to ignore the slam. "And, believe it or not, I've been working on it. And I've been making progress too." Moira almost confessed about kicking the pills but stopped herself short. Good grief, she wasn't that drunk. Oh, sure, she was feeling the effects, but she wasn't wasted. Not yet.

"Moira." Lisa put her hand on Moira's again. "I appreciate that you're still working through your grief and sorting things out with Alex. And I appreciate that you feel the need to get out among people again. But I honestly do not believe you are ready to return to work."

"But I am," Moira said loudly. "I really am."

"I need to go." Lisa was reaching for her purse, pulling out her wallet and then her phone. "I'm supposed to meet a client in a few minutes." She laid some cash on the table. "I hope you'll take care of yourself." Lisa stood up. "And maybe you should call a taxi, Moira. I don't—"

"Don't worry about me," Moira said angrily. "I'm just fine."

"It's just that I don't think you should drive like—"

Moira cut Lisa off with a foul word then, lifting her glass in a high toast, she watched as her former boss stormed out of the wine bar. So much for going back to work. That bridge was burnt now. Moira finished her wine then asked for the check and without looking at it, pocketed Lisa's cash, and handed the waiter her credit card. While he processed it, she polished off Lisa's wine too. Discretely. At least that was what she told herself.

Moira waited until she was out in her car to call her shrink. Sitting in the parking lot, she demanded to speak to him, and when he finally picked up, she started to make sobbing sounds and, claiming she was falling apart from grief and divorce problems, she begged him to call in a refill prescription for Diazepam, promising to make an appointment as soon as she calmed down. "I just can't function," she cried. "I feel like I'm dying."

By the time Moira was home, she couldn't even remember how she'd gotten there. But with her fresh prescription in her purse, she headed straight to her room. Her plan was to take these "chill" pills as prescribed, but wasn't sure she knew how. But she swallowed a single pill—with water—then fell into bed, sobbing for real. She had blown it big. Again.

Most people are glad to get time off from work, but I resent this holiday. Thanks to Independence Day I won't see Bernard for several days. If Dad was still at Larry's I'd invite Bernard over for another swim, but Dad moved out when Larry's wife and kids came home. I feel jealous to imagine them happily lounging around their pool. The happy family at home.

But Bernard couldn't spend time with me anyway. He and his dad and grandma drove to the beach last night for a small family reunion. Must be nice to have family that wants to reunite. I can't imagine. But that's what holidays are for. At least it used to be that way. I texted Dad this morning, hoping he might invite me to do something fun with him. But he was at the golf course—participating in a fundraiser tournament.

Although he promised to call later, I'm not holding my breath. It feels like he's done with us now. Like he's checked out, moved on, and probably planning for a brand new life of bachelorhood. Instead of renting a room like he'd said he was going to do, he rented a studio apartment right downtown. I haven't seen it yet, but he assured me it's small. "Not big enough for guests." And he claims it was the only thing available. Like we don't have spare rooms here that he could use—for free. Whatever.

I got a sweet text from Maddie today. She's having a pretty good summer and, despite my juvenile jealousy that Grandma is taking her and Kendall to an amusement park next week, I'm happy for her. I hope she has fun. She needs to do something besides read this summer.

And, thankfully, I'll be back at work by then. It was actually hard to tell the kids good-bye yesterday afternoon. But I was glad to hear that Sheena and Sicily were spending the weekend with their grandparents. So at least I don't need to worry about them. Because, despite my tip-off phone call several weeks ago, I know their mom is still neglecting them. And if things don't get better, I do plan to do something about it. I'm just not sure what. Maybe I'll ask Val to call someone. Anyway, it's torture to think about everyone spending fun times with their families for Independence Day. I guess my independence is that I'm free from all that. Independently alone.

Although Mom, as usual, is home, I haven't seen her for a few days. And right now I feel bored and sick of this silent house. So I decide to slip up to the tree house for a while—before it gets too hot. I haven't read much of Hannah's diary lately. Her happy, wonderful life makes me too miserable. And yet, I'm determined to read the whole thing. And, to be honest, I know that I've dragged it out for another reason. I feel like when I finish it to the end, I will lose this final connection with her. So I plan to make it last as long as possible. But today, since it's a holiday and I feel the need for some family time—even if it's with my dead sister—I make myself comfortable and open it up.

I know most girls think prom is the highlight event of high school, and maybe I felt like that last year when I was wishing I was a junior so I could go, but now that I am, it seems a little ho-hum. I suspect my lack of genuine interest is irritating my mother. But honestly, she's got enough enthusiasm for both of us. So I just sort of play along as we shop for a gown and shoes and all that. I remind her that it's just a one night thing, but she points out that I might be the only Josephson girl who will ever go to prom, therefore she will pull out the stops.

But I must admit I feel horrible to see how much it's costing. Of course, Mom never seems to concern herself with money when she's shopping. I've overheard arguments with Dad about this very thing. He's even accused her of being a shopping addict. I've jokingly called her a shopaholic before, but I never seriously meant it. Now I'm actually worried that she has a real shopping addiction problem. And I do wonder...can she really afford it?

Even if she can afford it, wouldn't it be better to send that money to a needy cause? Like poor orphans in Uganda? When she decided on an expensive pair of shoes for prom—that I know will only be worn once—I actually explained our church's outreach ministry for a village in Uganda, suggesting we donate the price of the shoes instead of buying them. But Mom just laughed. Then she checked my forehead for fever. I assured her that I was perfectly fine, but that I'd rather invest myself in something more worthwhile. And when I told her that I doubt I'll go to prom next year, she was so upset that she used it against me. It became *her excuse to go all out. So, not wanting to create a scene in the store, I just pasted on my happy face and cooperated. But, seriously, I'm concerned about her.*

It's hard to admit that my mom is shallow and materialistic, but it's true. She is all about image and keeping up with the Joneses. Except that she wants to BE the Joneses. And, sure, I used to be like that, but I don't want that anymore. Ever since I invited Christ into my heart, I see everyone and everything differently. At least I hope I do. I care more about others now—more than I ever have before. And I know I'm still selfish, but I don't want to be self-centered now. I guess that's the difference.

I've discovered it's painful to care so much about others. It's like laying your heart on the line. Becoming involved and vulnerable. Especially with my family. And not just my mom—although that's getting pretty painful. She resents that I'm changing. She even acts like she's losing me. But, seriously, I think she's just worried about losing her shopping buddy—her partner in crime.

The more I think about my family, the more I realize how much I love them…and how much they all need help. And even though I pray for them, I wish I could help more. I realize how much they need God's help. I hope and pray God will hurry up and bring it to them—before it all gets too messed up.

So...how are they messed up? Well, for starters no one wants to go to church anymore. Okay, I'll admit that I got a little bored with church too. Back before I really understood what it meant. Not that I understand everything—I really don't. But I get some of it, and I think Pastor Dan is doing the best he can. Even if his sermons seem dull at times. If you listen, you get something out of it. But everyone in my family has an excuse for not going.

Mom uses her work as her excuse. She almost always has an open house on Sundays. I wonder if she plans it that way on purpose. And Dad uses golf as his excuse. He claims he's golfing with clients, but I'm not sure that's completely true. Maddie doesn't like to go because she feels she's too old for Sunday school and too young for the worship service, even though she's probably smarter than most of the congregation. And Kiera, well, she just comes out and says she hates church—period. I have to give it to Kiera, she's probably the most honest about it. I respect her for that.

I close Hannah's diary with a tinge of satisfaction—and a lot of questions. It does feel good to think Hannah respected me—even though we didn't agree on spiritual things. And I'm feeling sorry for her again. I had no idea that she was so frustrated with Mom. I always thought they were such besties. And it makes me sad to realize she was so worried about our family. So much that she seemed sort of disconnected. Pretty weird since I always thought she had the inside track with our family. Well, except me—since it seems I was wrong about that too. And that bit about Mom being addicted to shopping catches me off guard. Oh, I know Mom used to shop—a lot. But I never thought much of it. And, quite honestly, it seems preferable to what she's addicted to now.

I'm also surprised to learn that Hannah was so unenthused about the prom last year. I seriously thought she loved all that crud. Once again, I feel confused over my dead sister's diary. On one hand, I'm relieved to see she's not all happy-happy-happy all the time. That was kind of scary. I can relate to this more serious side of Hannah. And it's sweet that she wanted to help orphans in Uganda.

But as I sit there in a slight stupor, trying to wrap my head around what I've just read, I still feel confused. It's like everything I believed has been turned upside down. When my life was unraveling, I thought I had everyone else all figured out. But my assumptions—I see now—were pretty much off. It's disturbing to realize that I'm not as smart as I thought I was.

I wonder what else I don't understand.

Twenty-One

WHEN MY RETREAT IN THE TREE STARTS TO feel like a slow cooker, I notice that my phone battery is getting low and decide it's time to go back inside the house. As if I'm going to hear from anyone, although I wish Bernard would text me. I asked him to send me a photo of the ocean. "So I can be justifiably jealous," I jokingly told him. The sad part is that it's true. I'm jealous of everyone who's spending time with family today. It makes me hate holidays. Maybe I'll start a new fad—kind of like being vegan. Instead of abstaining from animal proteins, I'll abstain from holidays.

As usual, it's cool and dark and quiet in my house. Kind of like I imagine a tomb or catacomb might feel— dead. I honestly don't know what's going on with Mom, but I get the impression it's not good. Sometimes I hear her knocking around late at night. And I think I've even heard her talking to herself, ranting like a crazy woman. I let Dad know that I was getting concerned for her sanity, but he just blew it off. He claims she needs to get low enough to *look up and ask for help*. I wonder if she'll be able to open her eyes and see anything by the time she gets that low.

I go into the kitchen to scrounge up something to eat. Not for the first time, I think it wouldn't be a bad idea for me to learn to cook. Except that I don't want to. But I'm getting tired of ramen noodles and mac and cheese and peanut butter. Those have been my usual standbys in recent months. I haven't really announced it officially to anyone, but I've given up, not only on being vegan and vegetarian, but pescetarian as well. It's just too hard to keep track of all these foods—the dos and the don'ts. It's exhausting. And I have enough in my life that wears me out. Why make food a part of it. Still, it's hard to get used to the freedom of eating with such…well, freedom. But being that it's Independence Day, I've got this strange hankering for fried chicken and barbecued ribs. Not that it's happening here. Maybe I'll swing by a fast food place and pig out.

"Why are you standing there with the refrigerator door open?" Mom says from behind me. Her tone is aggravated. Not that it's anything new.

"Because I'm looking for something to eat," I say without turning around.

"You've been *looking* for about ten minutes," she says.

I firmly close the door then turn to look at her. As expected, she looks like something the cat dragged in. Even worse than last week. Instead of getting mad, like I usually do, I actually feel sorry for her. How low does she plan to go? So, instead, of making some snarky remark about how there's never anything good to eat around here, or how I'm the only one who brings home groceries (thanks to Dad's financial contribution) I ask her how she's doing.

"Oh, I'm just great." She rolls her eyes. "Can't you tell by looking at me?"

I purse my lips, biting my sharp tongue and its comebacks. "Did you know that it's Independence Day?" I ask meekly. "Fourth of July?"

She shrugs then checks the coffeepot to see there's still some left. I get her a mug and watch as she fills it with some rather thick looking coffee. "Need some milk for that?" I offer.

"It's fine." She sits at the breakfast bar and, leaning desolately on her elbows, resembles something from skid row. I cringe as she takes a sip of that horrid looking coffee, but she doesn't even flinch. Maybe all her cheap booze has seared her taste buds. Or maybe she just doesn't care.

I sit down across from her and try to think of something to say. Something that's not snarky or mean or judgmental. I wonder what Bernard would suggest. He'd probably say, "Be honest but kind." That's just how he is. Me, not so much. Oh, I can do the honest part, but not kindly. Still, I'm willing to try.

"I'm worried about you, Mom."

She looks up from her coffee. "Huh?"

"I'm worried." I sigh. "You don't seem very healthy. I keep thinking you're going to get better—you know, back to your old self. But day after day, you just seem to stay the same." I want to say *you get worse* but realize that sounds pretty harsh. "It's like you're stuck. Like you can't get out of this thing...whatever it is."

"This *whatever* it is?" She narrows her eyes. "My firstborn child died and my husband left me, within six months of each other. And the cherry on top—I lost my job this week. That's *whatever* it is, Kiera."

"I'm aware of that, Mom." I try to keep my voice calm. "We've all been through a lot this year and—"

"Everyone else is holding up better than I am." She glares at me. "That's what you want to say, isn't it?"

"Not exactly. I don't think I'm doing that great. I've got my problems too."

"But you still manage to get up and go to work. You're not guzzling alcohol and popping pills." Mom looks regretful, like she hadn't meant to admit so much.

"So you're still doing that?" I say in a flat tone.

"That what?" She acts oblivious, but I can see through her.

"Pills. Like you just said. You're doping again? Opiates and alcohol?"

She shrugs. "It takes a little something to get through each day."

Okay, my patience has worn thin, and I realize I'm not very good at this. "What about *us*, Mom?"

"Who is *us*?"

"Maddie and me. You know, you still have two kids."

"Maddie can stay with her grandma as long as she needs to. Virginia called a few days ago. She assured me that Maddie is as *happy as a clam*—her exact words. And Virginia has offered to keep her indefinitely. They even went to visit the middle school. I'm sure she made this generous offer because Alex has complained to her about me. He thinks I'm a failure as a mother. Maybe he's right."

I want to point out that there's still me but don't see the point.

"And you obviously don't need me, Kiera. You never have."

"That's not true." I place my palms flat on the granite countertop, trying to control my temper. "I needed you as much as my sisters did, but you just never noticed." Now I narrow my eyes at her. "I know that you never wanted me, Mom. I've heard you joke with your friends—when you didn't think I was listening. You've said that I was un-planned and unwanted and nearly aborted—and you've always treated—"

"That's a lie!" She slams the mug down so hard I'm surprised it doesn't shatter.

"That is the *truth*, Mom. I heard you say those very words with my own ears."

"Well, then you misunderstood the meaning. I was probably just making light of my situation. After all, I had two kids in diapers simultaneously. That's stressful. I'm sure I was trying to be funny."

"It wasn't funny to me." I feel tears burning, but I will hold them back. "And I know why you named me after your mom—it's because you hated her and you hate me too!"

"That is not true." But she doesn't shout this time, and her brow is so deeply creased that I know I must've hit the mark. Or else she's overdue for Botox.

"Which part is not true?" I challenge. "That you hated your mom? Or that you hate me? I've heard you tell Dad that I'm just like your mother, and we all know how you felt about her. Any way you look at it, it's not good, Mom. Not a nice way to speak of your dearly departed mother. Not a nice way to treat your still living daughter."

She holds up a finger, and I can see that her hands are shaking. Does this mean she needs a drink or a pill...or that she's had too many? I'm not sure which it is, but I wait to see what's coming.

"First of all," she says slowly. "I loved my mother."

"Well, good for you." I know what this means. I'm the one she never loved. But I don't think I can take much more of this—and keep my tears at bay. Still, I stay there, waiting for her to tell me what I know is true.

She holds up a second finger now. "And I have always loved you too, Kiera. But you make it very difficult. You're not easy. You never have been."

"Maybe that's because I grew up knowing I was unwanted," I say in a sharp tone. "It must be difficult to love something you don't want. Even your own child. And you obviously didn't *need* a second child, Mom. You already had the perfect one. A beautiful blue-eyed blonde with a sweet disposition. A miniature replica of yourself. Why would you need or want anything else? I'm surprised you didn't get that abortion with me. I'll bet you wished you had. Sometimes I do too. And what about Maddie? Was she a mistake too? But she's easier to get rid of. Ship her off to Grandma. Well, I'm easy to get rid of too. I'll take care of that for you." And before she can respond, I run out of there.

But I don't go up to my room. I head straight for the garage. I hop on my bike and take off. I don't know where I'm going, but I have to get away—from her. Maybe I'll ride down to the river and take a flying leap off of the tallest bridge and just end this thing. Who would care?

Twenty-Two

MOIRA FELT SICK. NOT JUST FROM PILLS AND booze either. She felt sick over what Kiera had just said. And even sicker to admit that Kiera was partly right. She had said some of those things. Still, it was horrible to hear those words again—spoken aloud. Horrible to realize that Kiera had heard snippets of those conversations—and as a child. How long had she been harboring those words inside of her? How much damage might it have done?

Moira had gone after Kiera when she'd realized she wasn't going to her room. But by the time she reached the garage, finding Kiera and her bike were gone, Moira couldn't think straight—didn't know what to do. She'd stood for a few long minutes on the concrete step trying to figure it out. Should she go after Kiera? But where had she gone? And did Moira really want to drive under the influence? She still remembered the scorn in Lisa's eyes that day at the wine bar, horrified that Moira might actually drive in that condition. Yet how many times had Moira done just that? As a result, she'd removed her car key from the ring and hurled it out into the backyard. She could probably find it if she searched for a few hours, but the missing key was enough to keep her from jumping behind the wheel.

Moira felt the heat from the sun-baked driveway radiating into the garage. It was so hot out, Kiera wouldn't last long on her bike. She'd probably be back soon. Or she'd be with Alex. Moira pushed the button to close the garage door then went back into the house and closed the door. Something had to change. She couldn't go on like this. Not only was she ruining her own life, she was ruining the lives of the people she loved. And despite what Kiera believed, Moira did love her.

But it was a strange sort of love. Not so different than the love she felt for her mother. She loved them both intensely—even if she didn't understand them—and when they hurt her, as they often did, it cut her to the core. Like that old song, "You only hurt the ones you love."

Feeling desperate and determined, Moira went to her room and, gathering up her pills and booze, she carried it into her bathroom. She had to make a choice—there were two options. Only two. For some reason it seemed crystal clear right now. She had reached a crossroads in life. She could turn left or turn right. The left turn—she could wash down the last of her pills with a couple of liters of vodka and permanently check out. Or the right turn, she could dump it all down the toilet. Flush it once and for all.

She knew that right was right, but the left turn sounded easier. End of her pain. End of hurting others. And maybe, if God was real and if Moira prayed one last sinner's prayer, she might end up with Hannah at the end of the day. Hannah had always been so kind and loving and compassionate. Hannah would understand. And, if God was real, he would understand too. At least Moira hoped so.

Not wanting to make up her mind in haste, she considered her other option. But the right turn path sounded too difficult, too painful, too impossible. After all, she'd tried to quit pills and booze before. It always started with two steps forward and one step back…and then two steps backward and one step forward…and finally it was nothing but backward, backward, backward. Failure upon failure upon failure. She knew she couldn't take more failure. She was too weak…too broken…too far gone. This was unfixable.

Moira filled a water-glass with vodka then emptied the bottle of pills into her trembling hand. She prayed her sinner's prayer then systematically took the pills, one by one, washing each one down with by a big slug of vodka. Again and again, until the last pill was gone and the two liter bottle was empty. At last, it was over. She was done. Peace…was coming.

I pedal furiously toward the river. I am so angry I can barely string my thoughts together. But one thing I know—*I am so done with this.* So over it! I can't take it anymore. Not for one more day. Here I am trying my best to just get by. But my mom is making me crazy. Seriously freaking crazy. And it has to end. It ends *today!*

Oh, I don't really intend to throw myself off of a bridge. I'm not crazy. Just mad. Although it's so hot out, I might take a quick dip from the bank just to cool off. But as I pedal down to the park, I'm putting together a plan. And, really, I think it's about time. I've been patient enough. Especially when you consider I am not a patient person.

As I wheel my bike through the river park, where families are enjoying their July Fourth picnics, pitching horse shoes and corn hole, playing badminton and volleyball, I have made up my mind. If Dad refuses to let me live with him, I will start talking to a social worker about being emancipated. The sooner I'm on my own, the better. After all, my sanity is at sake.

And even if I wind up in foster care or a group home, it sounds less painful than living with my whacked-out mom. And that is how I plan to put it to my dad. As soon as I can get him to answer his phone. I've called and texted him and, worried that my phone's just minutes from dead, I'm about to turn it off when I notice a text from my mom. I'm tempted to ignore it but decide to take a quick peek before I jump into the river.

> All I can say, Kiera, is that I'm sorry. I never wanted you to go through so much pain. I do love you. I will always love you. Please, remember that. As I set myself free, I will be setting you free. And Maddie too. I will be with Hannah soon. Don't cry for me. Happy Independence Day. I love you.
>
> Mom

I'm too stunned to process this. Does this mean what I think it means? I read it again and realize that I'm not imagining things. Mom is about to take her life. As I dial 911 with shaking fingers, I know she could do it. She could absolutely do it. This has been one of my biggest fears—that I'd come home to find her dead.

The 911 operator answers quickly, and I began to blurt out my emergency. "My mother is taking her life," I sob into my phone. "Right now. She just texted me about it." Then I give Mom's name and address and my fear that she's overdosed on opiates and alcohol. I even explain that she's probably in her bedroom. I describe the location of the room and that Mom's door has a deadbolt. "They might have to kick the door in," I blurt. "Please, hurry! It might be too late."

As tears streak down my face, the operator assures me

that paramedics are on their way, continuing to ask me questions about the time frame in such a calm tone, I wonder if she really gets it. I quickly explain about how long I've been gone and when Mom texted. "But I know this is real!" I shout at her. "I know she could do it. She's depressed and drinking and using opiates. And her text said she wants to be with my dead sister."

The woman asks me what that means, and I have to explain that Hannah died six months ago. But now I'm crying so hard I can hardly speak at all. "Are they helping her?" I sob into my phone.

"They're on their way. But where are you right now?"

"River Park, but please help my—"

"I want you to go to the south parking lot and watch for a patrol car," she instructs. "I'm sending someone out to meet you." I tell her I'm on my way, but as I wheel my bike back through the busy park, my phone goes silent. My battery is dead. I pocket my phone and hop on my bike, pedaling fast to the parking lot. It's not long until I see a patrol car.

A female officer gets out of the passenger side, hurrying toward me. "I'm Lieutenant Rogers. Let's leave your bike here." But my hands are shaking so much that she has to help me lock my bike in the rack.

"Have they got her yet?" I ask as we go to the patrol car where her partner is waiting behind the wheel. "Is she alive?"

"We don't know anything for sure right now," he tells

me. "But I'm sure paramedics have reached your house by now. And if your mother needs medical assistance, they'll stabilize her before they transport."

"Where are we going?" I ask.

"To the hospital," Lieutenant Rogers tells me.

"I need to charge my phone," I say. "So I can call my dad."

"Want my phone?" she offers.

"I, uh, I can't remember his number right now. It's in my phone."

"We'll find a charger at the hospital," she tells me. "You can call from there."

At the Emergency entrance, Lieutenant Rogers goes in with me. And soon I'm giving my mom's information to the reception clerk. As best I can anyway. I keep asking if anyone knows anything, but I'm getting no answers. Finally, the reception clerk makes a phone call and seems to learn something.

"They're transporting her now," she tells me.

"So she's alive?"

"I can't say anything about her condition."

"Come sit down," Lieutenant Rogers tells me. "Let me have your phone and I'll see if I can find a charger."

By the time she returns with a phone cord, I hear the sound of an ambulance siren. I go to the door, hoping to see if it's Mom, but the vehicle goes around a corner and Lieutenant Rogers tells me I need to stay here. "That entrance is for emergency personnel only. Why don't you call your dad?"

To my relief, Dad answers, and I manage to stammer out the news about Mom. I can tell he's shocked, but he also sounds slightly angry. "I can't believe she'd do that to us. But I'm on my way," he says sharply. "I'll be there in about twenty minutes."

I tell Lieutenant Rogers that my dad is coming, and she apologizes for having to go, but explains that it's a holiday and patrol cars are needed on the streets. I thank her and assure her I'll be okay. But I feel far from okay. And as I wait for Dad to get there—or to hear what's happening with Mom or if she's even alive—it feels like the longest twenty minutes of my life.

When Dad arrives, still wearing his golf clothes, he immediately takes over. He talks to the reception clerk and insists on going into the ER to speak to a doctor. And now I'm waiting again, still unsure as to whether Mom is alive or not. And, once again, I am blaming myself for the death of not just one family member, but two. Mom wouldn't be such a mess if Hannah hadn't died. Hannah wouldn't have died if I hadn't called for a ride that night. Mom wouldn't be in the ER if I hadn't told her that I knew she hated me…

What is wrong with me? What is wrong with our family?

"You look like you need a friend."

"Huh?" I look up to see the kind, wrinkled face of an

elderly woman—and the bluest eyes I think I've ever seen. Almost the same shade as Hannah's eyes.

"I've been watching you, dear, and you seem very upset. Is someone you know in trouble?"

I nod mutely.

"A loved one?"

"My mother," I blurt. "She might be dead."

"Oh, dear. Poor child." She sits beside me. "What happened?"

"She—she may have taken her life." And suddenly I'm telling this stranger about Hannah's death and our messed-up family. "And the last thing I said to my mom was that I knew she didn't love me."

"All mothers love their children, dear. I'm sure your mother loves you too."

"I, uh, I don't know. I mean, she loved Hannah so much. And she's blamed me for Hannah's death." I even tell her about how I called home for a ride that night...on New Year's Eve. "But I didn't know the roads were icy," I sob. "Or that Hannah was the one who would pick me up."

"Of course you didn't. And it wasn't your fault, dear. You can't blame yourself for something that someone else does. Something you have no control over. Not unless you are God." She smiles sadly. "And I don't think you're God...are you?"

I consider her words—as crazy as they sound, they

make a strange sort of sense. "No, I'm not God," I mutter. "Of course not."

"May I pray with you, dear?"

"I, uh, I guess so." I don't confess to her that I doubt God, if he's even there, will listen to anything that concerns me. Why should he?

She asks me my name and, after I tell her, she takes both my hands in hers then bows her head. "Dear Heavenly Father. Your child Kiera is here with me. I know you can see her, Lord, and that you want her to know how much you love her and her family. I pray that you will be with Kiera's dear mother right now. Lord, I pray that you will reach down and touch this poor woman with your unconditional love. I pray that you will help the physicians ministering to her to help her with the same sort of healing wisdom that you, our Great Physician, would bestow with your own loving hands. I pray that you would use this whole situation for your glory, Lord. I ask that you heal all of Kiera's family. Most of all, I ask you to heal Kiera. Help her to see how much you love her—how much you love all of them. Pour out your never-ending mercies upon each of them, Lord. Give them a miracle." She lets out a long sigh. "Amen."

Still holding my hands, she looks at me. "God is the perfect controller of all things," she says quietly. "And he is the miracle maker."

I don't really understand her words, but I simply nod, grateful for her kindness. We both sit there for a few minutes, and then I hear Dad calling my name. "I've got to go," I tell her. "But thank you."

Her smile is like sunshine. "It'll be okay, dear. I just know it."

I'm not so sure, but as I hurry toward my dad, I don't feel quite as frightened as I did before. But maybe that's due to his expression. He seems relieved. "Your mother's going to be okay," he tells me. And now I break into full blown tears. But he hugs me. "I'm sorry you had to go through this, honey. It's too much for a kid to bear."

"It's—it's okay," I sob. "I was just so scared…that she was dead."

"She would've been dead, Kiera. If you hadn't called 911 when you did. The doctor said that the information you gave the paramedics was the difference between life and death for your mom. He said they got there just in time. He even called it slightly miraculous."

"Miraculous?"

"Because you said that you thought she'd ODed on opiates. And because the paramedics were carrying Naloxone."

"What's that?"

"A drug that helps to reverse the effect of the drugs she'd consumed. They immediately administered it to her. That's what saved her life. And it's relatively new for paramedics to carry that drug with them. The doctor called it a miracle."

I turn to look for the old lady—I want to tell her the

good news—but I don't see her anywhere. And I realize, sadly, I never got her name. But I won't forget her prayer... or how she spoke of a miracle.

Twenty-Three

EVEN THOUGH MOM IS ALIVE, SHE'S NOT out of the woods. At least that's what Dad tells me after another consultation with the doctor. "They'll continue to administer Naloxone as well as some other things," he says as we set our cafeteria food on a table.

"Is she conscious?" I take a sip of what turns out to be flat tasting soda.

"I'm not sure. But the doctor says she's not ready for visitors."

"Are you going to see her when she is?" I squirt ketchup into my fry basket.

He shrugs as he stirs cream into his coffee. "I honestly don't know. It might not be a good idea. I don't want to upset her."

"She wouldn't be upset if you two were getting back together," I say hopefully.

"I can't promise anything, Kiera. Just because your mom tried to kill herself doesn't change what was wrong between us. It just shows that she's more broken than any of us realized."

"Oh." I try to hide my disappointment as I sip my soda. I want to ask him what was wrong between them but feel this isn't the time. And the hospital cafeteria isn't the place.

"The doctor is recommending rehab treatment for her...when she gets released from the hospital."

"When will that be?"

"Not for a few days. That'll give me time to get something set up." He frowns. "Unfortunately, that's not covered on my insurance plan. And it won't be cheap."

I don't know what to say about this. How do you put a price tag on someone's life? "How long do you think she'll be in treatment?" I ask meekly.

"The doctor recommends at least thirty days. And he gave me a list of places."

"Oh." I try to imagine my mom gone for a whole month. To be honest, it seems like she's been gone anyway, but it will be weird not to have her in the house at all. "Are you going to move back home?" I stare down at the soggy fries that I've barely touched.

"Do you need me to?" His brow creases. "I mean, I realize you're only sixteen, and if you need me there, I will move back. But I'll hold onto my apartment—for when Mom comes home. I can't live there after that."

I can tell he doesn't really want to move back home. "You don't have to leave your apartment if you don't want to." I try to act nonchalant. "I'll be fine."

"It's just that it's so close to work. And with coworkers taking vacations, I've been pretty busy at work. It's handy living nearby."

"Yeah, I guess that makes sense."

"But, really, Kiera, if you need me to be home, I'll pack up and move back."

"No, Dad. That's not necessary." I force a smile. "I'm pretty independent. And if I need anything, I'll just call you."

"And I'll keep giving you grocery money and all that," he promises. "And maybe I can come home during the weekend."

"Sure." I nod. "That'd be good."

"And I don't think we should tell Maddie about this."

I question this at first but then consider how Maddie would react and realize he's right. "Yeah, she doesn't need any more stress."

"None of us do." Dad checks his watch. "I want to go by the house and take care of some things."

"Some things?"

"Yeah. I guess the paramedics had to break in. Might need to get a locksmith out there and whatnot. Do you want to go home with me?"

"What about Mom?"

"She probably won't even know we're gone."

"I'd rather stay here."

He nods. "Yeah, that's probably a good idea. I'll get things figured out at home then come back for you."

Now I remember my bike. I explain to Dad about leaving it at the park and he promises to get a friend with a pickup to get it for me. I give him my bike lock key and then he leaves. I poke at my fries awhile but have no appetite. I feel so alone right now as I dump the remainders of my lunch in the trash. I look around, hoping to see the kind old lady with the clear blue eyes, but she seems to have vanished. And, as strange as it seems—especially for someone like me—I can't help but wonder if she was even real. It's not that I think I imagined her, but something about her was so unworldly. If I believed in such things, I might even wonder if she was some sort of angel. Perhaps even Hannah in disguise.

Feeling like I'm going slightly crazy, I wander back to the ER waiting area. As I go, I keep my eyes peeled for that old lady. But I don't see her. And when I ask a couple of people in the waiting area, they don't seem to have seen her either. Weird. I check in at the reception desk, asking if there's been any change with my mom or if she's able to have visitors. It takes awhile for her to check. But then she pretty much reiterates what my dad said about her condition. "Can someone let me know if anything changes?" I ask. "I mean, if she can have visitors or anything."

"Of course." The woman smiles patiently, but her eyes seem blank. I'm sure she must answer the same sort of questions to the same sort of people every single day. What a job.

I sit back down and continue charging my phone on the borrowed cord, while alternately watching the TV, which is tuned to a Disney channel, and reading old magazines. What a way to spend the Fourth of July. My personal independence day. I remind myself of my goal to get emancipated. It seems that's not necessary now. Life has emancipated me. From all members of my family. At least for thirty days. What happens after that is anyone's guess. I do not feel hopeful.

It's past seven by the time I'm allowed to see my mom. With her eyes closed and looking so pale and still, I'm not sure she's really alive. She's got an IV and what must be oxygen tubes in her nose. I stand there silently watching, relieved to see that her chest is slowly rising and falling. I hate to disturb her but feel the need to say something. Something encouraging.

"I love you, Mom," I whisper. "I'm sorry I don't show it more."

Her eyes flutter open. "Kiera." Her voice sounds hoarse.

"I'm sorry...." I feel tears coming again, but I'm determined to hold them back.

"I'm sorry too." Her blue eyes fill with tears. "So sorry."

"You're going to get better." I reach for her hand, careful not to bump her IV connection. "We're all going to get better."

"I…hope…so." Her eyes close again.

"Just rest," I tell her. "Don't worry about anything. Dad's here to help me. And we're not telling Maddie about this."

"Thank…you." Her eyelashes flutter.

"I'll let you rest," I say quietly. And then I do something I haven't done in years. I lean down and kiss her cheek. "I do love you, Mom. I'm just not good at showing it."

"I love you too, Kiera," she whispers. "I'm so sorry."

"We'll talk more tomorrow," I promise. "Just get well."

As I leave the room, I feel more love for my mother than I can ever remember feeling before. Oh, I loved her as a child. And I did all the usual things, making her birthday cards and Mother's Day cards and all that. But I always felt like there was a shadow over me. Like my older sister's light was so bright I could only be darkness in comparison. And then there was Maddie, stealing the attention that goes with being the baby. But I never stopped loving her. It's just that I stopped showing it. As a young teenager, I started to pull away…and I just kept pulling, until it was a habit I didn't know how to break. But maybe it's been broken now. I'm not sure. But time will tell.

I go outside to call Dad, telling him about my short visit with Mom. Then he informs me that my bike's been picked up and that he's nearly done with the locksmith and just finishing cleaning things up at the house. I assume that "cleaning things up" is related to Mom's suicide attempt. I really don't want to know.

"I'll come pick you up in a few minutes," he promises. And I tell him I'll meet him outside.

By the time Dad picks me up, I'm actually hungry. I express this to him, and he suggests a fast food stop.

"I'm craving a cheeseburger and chocolate milkshake," I tell him.

"What's this?" he asks with a shocked expression.

"Yeah, I'm giving it up," I admit sheepishly. "It's just too hard. I don't need more hard in my life right now."

"Well, I'm sorry about the hard part, but I must confess I'm relieved to hear this, Kiera. Welcome back to the carnivore carnival."

I roll my eyes at his bad joke, but I feel a tiny bit of relief to see this attempt at humor. Like my old dad is back. "How about Sonic?" I suggest.

"You're reading my mind." He slaps the steering wheel. "This is like old times. We'll sit in the drive-in side and pig out."

"And if we eat slowly enough, we might even see the fireworks from there."

"Sounds good to me," he says.

To my surprise, after burgers and fireworks, Dad decides to spend the night at the house. I try not to show how relieved I am that he does this, but something about being alone in a house where your mom just tried to kill herself is unsettling. I'm a little disappointed that he chooses to sleep in the guest room—not his old bedroom—but I understand. And the next morning, Dad and I both wake up early. I make us some coffee then call the hospital to check on my mom's condition.

"Sounds like she's doing better," I tell Dad as I fill a cup with coffee.

"How about I take you to breakfast?" he offers. "Then we could swing by the hospital if you like."

"That sounds good. I really feel like I need to be there for Mom."

"I appreciate that. And when you see her, you can tell her that I'm getting her rehab treatment all set up. I think I found a nice place with an opening next week. I spoke to the woman yesterday, and she told me to look at the website. It looks like a pretty place."

"So you don't plan to talk to Mom yourself?"

"As much as I'd like to, it's awkward right now. To be honest, I'm not sure it's in her best interest. Or that she would even want to see me."

"Maybe I'll ask her about that." I watch for his reaction, curious as to whether he actually wants to see her, but it's hard to tell. "Do you still love Mom?" I ask.

"I'm sure I'll always love her," he says sadly. "But the

truth is I don't like her much right now. I guess I haven't liked her for a while."

"You mean since Hannah died."

He frowns. "To be honest, it was before that."

"Why?" I press. "What happened?"

"I don't know. I guess she changed. Maybe we both changed. But when she started selling real estate, she seemed to lose interest in a lot of things."

"You mean like home things? Like cooking and stuff."

"Yeah...and other things too." His brow creases as he sips his coffee. "And she got so into shopping and spending money. It just felt like our world was spinning out of control. Like our family was coming apart."

I remember Hannah's diary and how she seemed to notice these same things.

"And then when Hannah died... Well, it's no secret that your mom blames me for that. And justifiably so. But what can I do? It's not like I don't miss Hannah as much as anyone. But you can only punish yourself for so long. At least that's what my therapist tells me. He's encouraged me to give up torturing myself over it. I can't say I'm there yet, but it's a goal. And I've found some things, like work and golf, help take my mind off it."

I notice that he's still wearing yesterday's golf clothes. "Do you have a golf date today?"

"I do, but not until ten. And I can cancel—"

"No need to cancel," I say as I pour the last of my coffee down the sink. "Let me grab a few things and I'll be ready to go." One of the things I intend to get is Hannah's diary. For whatever reason, I feel the need to read it. Maybe the whole thing too. I think I'm ready for it now.

It's around eleven by the time I'm allowed to go visit my mom. She's been moved to a different part of the hospital and looks a little more like herself today. She's sitting up in bed and, although she still has the IV, the oxygen tube is gone.

"How are you doing?" I ask as I stand by her bed.

"Okay…I guess." She looks down at her hands, picking at the edge of the tape that holds her IV needle in place.

"I'm sure this is hard," I say slowly, trying to think of the right things to say. "But I think it could be a good beginning for you."

She looks up. "A beginning?"

"Yeah." I nod. "Getting free from addictions. It'll be like a new beginning."

She sighs. "Oh…yeah. I guess so."

"Dad thinks he's found a good rehab treatment center for you."

She looks up with a slightly alarmed expression. "What?"

"The doctor recommended it. He wants you to go directly to it from here, Mom."

"Oh?" Her eyes are taking on that somewhat defiant expression.

"I don't think you'll get released from here unless you do." Okay, I have no idea about this and don't even care if it's a flat out lie. I know Mom needs treatment.

"I see." She slowly nods.

"Don't you want to get better?" I ask.

"Yes, of course." She purses her lips. "But rehab treatment?"

"Mom"—I try to soften my tone—"you ODed on opiates."

She looks down again. "I know."

"You need help. And because we love you, we want you to get help."

"Dad too?" she asks.

"Of course. Dad loves you, Mom. He told me so this morning."

"Oh...." She lets out a tired sigh.

"Do you want me to go?" I ask. "So you can rest?"

"No," she says quickly. "Not yet."

"Okay." I fiddle with the strap of my backpack, halfway tempted to extract Hannah's diary and read from it. I just finished a section that I think Mom needs to hear. But I don't want to upset her by confessing I stole my sister's diary. Not yet anyway.

"Sit." She points to a nearby chair.

I pull it closer to her bed then sit down.

"I need to talk to you," she says quietly.

"Okay." I cross my legs, waiting.

"Kiera. You know that's my mother's name."

"I know."

"She was a strong woman. Like you."

I consider this. Mostly I've heard that my grandmother was an alcoholic who drank herself to death. But instead of questioning Mom, I wait.

"You didn't know her. I mean before—before she started drinking. But she'd been a strong, intelligent woman." She paused to take in a deep breath. "She raised all of us kids completely on her own. She and my grandma."

"Because your dad died in Vietnam? When you were just a baby?"

"That's right. My mom and my grandma took care of us. Mom went to work and Grandma stayed home to cook and clean and all that. Then, not long after I got married, my grandma died. And that's when my mom started to fall apart. Her kids were all grown. Her mother was gone. And that's when Mom started to drink."

"Because she was alone?"

"I guess so. She was sort of lost." She bites her lip. "Kind of how I've been lately."

"Because of losing Hannah?"

"I think it actually began even before that. I'm not sure how exactly, but it seemed like I started to falling apart. Then losing Hannah finished me off."

This actually makes sense—melds with what Dad said and what I've read in Hannah's diary. Mom was unraveling before Hannah died. I don't know what to say and so I just say, "I'm sorry."

"That's what I need to tell you, Kiera. *I'm* sorry. I'm sorry you felt like I didn't love you—"

"I know you loved me, Mom. You loved me the best you could."

"But I wasn't a good mother to you. I never felt like I quite understood you."

"I know."

"You were always deeper than Hannah. I didn't know how to handle it. Hannah was easy. Well, until she started to change."

"Change?" This interests me. Did Mom realize what Hannah was going through in the last year before she died?

"She changed, Kiera. She lost interest in the things I liked to do. She didn't want to spend as much time with me." Mom looks at me with teary eyes. "It felt like she was becoming more like you. Or maybe she was just growing up."

"I think she was growing up," I tell her. "Hannah went through a whole lot of things, Mom. Stuff we never knew about."

Mom's brow creases. "How do you know that? You and Hannah weren't close. Not in that last year. You were living in your own world, and Hannah... I'm not sure what world she was living in. Just that it wasn't mine."

Her eyes get misty again. "I started to miss Hannah even before she died."

"I know," I say quietly.

Mom looks confused. "But how do you know? I've never told that to anyone."

"Because I've been getting to know Hannah better."

"What are you saying? How is that possible?"

I decide it's time to confess. "I found her diary, Mom. I've been reading it."

Mom's eyes grow large, and I can tell she's about to get angry.

"I know it was wrong—at first, anyway. But the more I read, the more I think Hannah wants me to read it. Almost like she planned for me to read it. Her diary is connecting me to her. Making me understand who she really was. And it wasn't who I thought she was. Probably not who any of us thought she was. And I'm actually learning stuff. Important stuff. And, anyway, I just know that Hannah is glad I'm reading it. And I think she would want you to read it too. When you're better."

Mom looks completely stunned, but she doesn't say a word.

"I can tell you're tired," I say. "I'm sure you need your rest."

"Yes…I am tired."

"I'll be here in the hospital," I assure her. "And I've got my phone. If you want to reach me, just call."

"Thank you."

As I leave, I feel sorry that I confessed about Hannah's diary. I know it has upset her. But sometimes the medicine we need doesn't taste so good. We need it anyway, though, if we want to get better.

Twenty-Four

IT'S LATE AFTERNOON BY THE TIME MOM calls me, asking me to come visit with her again. To my relief, she sounds more like herself. And as I ride the elevator up, I hope that she's either forgotten about the diary or forgiven me.

But as soon as I enter her room, I know that neither of those things have happened. Mom still looks aggravated. And I know why.

"I'm sorry if it upset you to hear about me reading Hannah's diary," I begin. "But you need to understand it's been really good for me. What she writes makes sense to me. And it's stretching me…and changing me…in ways I never expected."

"Well, I honestly do not know what to say." She folds her arms in front of her with a scowl. "I cannot believe you would do something like this, Kiera. Reading Hannah's diary." She shakes her head with disapproval.

"I felt guilty at first," I admit. "But the more I read, the more I believe Hannah left it behind for a reason. She wanted me to read it. I think she might want us all to read it."

"That's insane."

"You don't understand, Mom. But that's because you haven't read it. How about if I read a page or two to you?" I offer.

Her expression is shocked, like I just offered to shoot up in front of her. "No, Kiera, that's just wrong."

But I'm not ready to give up. "Reading Hannah's diary makes it almost seem like she's still here," I say. "Like she's alive. And according to her beliefs, she *is* alive. And I have to admit that I'm starting to wonder if she was right about some things."

Mom's brows arch with curiosity.

"I just read a section today," I press on. "It was really encouraging. I think it might encourage you too."

"Fine." She sounds reluctant but leans back. "Go ahead and read—if you must."

"Okay. Hannah wrote this particular piece on her seventeenth birthday. A year ago in August." I pull out the diary, open to the place I have in mind and begin to read.

I am seventeen today and more excited about
life than ever before. Even though this has probably

been the hardest year of my life, I feel like I'm able
to put the pain behind me and move forward. In
fact, I feel like dancing forward—and singing as
I go. And my happiness isn't related to anything
that's going on around me. Because the truth is,
things aren't going that well at home.

Even though I pray for them every day, nothing has changed with my family. Dad is still a
workaholic. Mom is still a shop-aholic. Maddie is
a book-aholic. And Kiera is a rebel-aholic—she's
opposed to everything. To be fair, I suppose I'm a
God-aholic. Because I can't live without God. So
I guess we're just a bunch of addicts around here.

The only difference is that my addiction makes
me happy and fulfilled. The rest of my family...
well, not so much. From what I can see, their addictions seem to make them more miserable. Dad's
hardly ever at home and when he is home, he's a
grouch. Mom's freaking over her bills but still
wanting something more. Maddie claims she has
no friends, but how's that possible if she's always
got her nose in a book? And Kiera, well, she just
seems outspoken and opposed and not particularly
happy.

I know it's wrong to judge them, and I will try
to keep my observations and opinions to myself. I
just hope and pray they can exchange their various
addictions for a God addiction. And it's only be-

cause I want them to be happy—the way my God addiction has made me happy.

In the past five months, God has helped me to grow and change and to become a truly better person—in ways that people can't even see. And that's fine, because that's not the point—I'm not on this journey to get approval from others. It's between God and me. I love how God is already giving me a direction and a purpose for my life. A hope and enthusiasm I never really had before. Oh, I used to pretend to be enthused over everything, but it was often an act—and the older I got, the harder it was to carry it off. Until it felt like I was just pretending all the time, acting like everything was peachy—when it really stank.

So here's what I'm really stoked about right now. And I haven't told anyone this—and probably won't until it's time for college—but I've decided that I want to pursue a career focused on children. More specifically, I want to do something that will help children in need, something that will improve their lives. I'm not sure if it will be orphaned children on the other side of the planet or neglected kids just down the street, but I just really want to help children.

I first came to this realization while baby-sitting Marnie and Kent's two pre-school aged kids. Originally I agreed to baby-sit in order to earn money for the summer camp that's coming up next week. Taking care of Jordie and Leah has been really cool. I've witnessed firsthand how children are so special. They're honest and loving and fun. And, as cliché as it sounds, they are our future. I just want to do something to help make their world a better place. With God's help, I will.

The reason I don't want to tell anyone about this new direction is because I know that they—my family at least—would probably make fun of me. Even Maddie, who's only eleven but doesn't really consider herself to be a little kid anymore, would probably think it's silly. And Kiera would probably think it a childish goal—she's so smart she probably plans to find ways to stop global warming and preserve the environment. And Mom would probably think working with kids doesn't sound glamorous enough. She always says I should pursue acting or run for Miss America. Ha! And Dad, well, he'd want me to have a solid career with a good 401(k) and good benefits.

But here by myself in my room, with just God and me and my diary, I do hereby declare that I plan to spend my life helping children in need. I realize it's not a lofty goal. But it makes me incredibly happy to imagine doing this. For starters, I will start planning a fundraiser for the orphans in Uganda. And then I'll just see where God leads me

from there. I've never been so excited about any-
thing. Happy Birthday to Me!

When I stop reading, I see tears streaking down Mom's face. And they do not appear to be tears of joy. "I'm sorry, Mom." I put the diary away and reach for her hand. "I didn't mean to upset you."

"I—I just didn't—didn't know," she sobs. "I didn't know—any of this."

I reach for the tissue box, handing it to her, waiting as she blows her nose and wipes her eyes. "I guess I shouldn't have read that," I say quietly. "I didn't realize it would—"

"Hannah really wrote *that*?" Mom blinks then reaches for another tissue. "You're certain she wrote that?"

"Of course. It's Hannah's handwriting and her diary, I got it from her room. She wrote it."

"I just never knew." Mom lets out a ragged sigh, still blotting her tears. "She sounds like a stranger."

"I didn't know it would make you sad, Mom. I actually felt kind of happy to read it."

"Happy?" Mom looks sincerely shocked. "How could that possibly make anyone happy?"

"It's just so genuine—and such depth of feeling. Hannah sounded truly glad to think she was going to help children. And remember that fundraiser she organized with the church last fall? They made several thousand dollars. Everyone was talking about how wonderful that was. They were still talking about it at her memorial service. Remember?"

Mom closes her eyes, leaning back into her pillows. "I—I just don't think I can take any more. This is too hard."

"I'm sorry, Mom. I honestly didn't know it would upset you like this. I thought you'd be encouraged to hear how happy Hannah was—and it was a real sort of happiness. Not superficial."

"That's enough, Kiera." She waves a dismissive hand. "I need to rest now."

"Yes, of course. I'm sorry."

I get up and make my way, as quietly as I can, from her room.

By the next day, Mom appears to have forgiven me for reading to her from Hannah's diary. In fact, it seems like she wants to talk about it. At first she skirts around the issue, inquiring as to how and where I found the diary— and how many times had I snuck into Hannah's room? I confess I borrowed a swimsuit once, and accidentally discovered the diary, snitching it the next day.

"Have you read the whole thing?" she asks.

"I'm in October now," I confess. "She's just getting the fundraiser going and is really excited about it."

"Yes, yes... I do remember that now. Barely. I wasn't very involved with church when all that was going on."

"I know. Me neither."

"So how long will it be until you finish reading?" Mom's tone sounds impatient.

"To start with, I was reading it kind of slowly. Making myself take it in smaller portions because it made me feel connected to Hannah, and I didn't want to break that connection when it ended. It's weird—I feel more connected to her now than when she was alive. Well, except for when we were kids. Anyway, I didn't want her diary to end. But now I've decided that I will just read through it quickly. And then I can read it all over again, whenever I feel a need to connect with her."

Mom frowns. "So do you know when the diary ends? What time of year?"

"I've controlled myself from peeking at the end," I explain. "But based on the pages left, I'm guessing there are at least two more months." I don't want to admit that I suspect it goes to late December or that I'm almost afraid to read the final entry…the last time she writes before the accident. It will probably be painful.

"You said that it's changed you," Mom says carefully. "Or that it's changing you. What do you mean by that?"

"Well, I used to be an atheist. At least that's what I used to tell Hannah. Probably just to frustrate her because it seemed like she was getting so involved in church and her youth group friends. Then, after Hannah died, I decided I was agnostic."

"Meaning you believe in God's existence, but don't care?"

"Yeah, that pretty much describes it. But to be more honest, I felt like God didn't really care about me."

Mom grimaces.

"Anyway, I'm starting to question a lot of things about myself and my beliefs. For the first time, I'm curious about the way Hannah related to God. She was so sold out and certain and made it sound personal. But if Hannah talked about her faith when she was alive, I would either argue or make fun of her. I never gave her a chance to really tell me about it. I thought I already knew it all." I purse my lips, seeing what a stupid arrogant brat I've been. Wishing it had all been different. But now it's too late.

Mom reaches for a piece of paper. "Well, I'm going to be transferred to the rehab facility on Tuesday. Someone printed this list for me—things I can bring." She hands it to me. "I thought maybe you could pack them up for me and drop them by here tomorrow. After work. I know you have work."

I glance at the list and nod. "Yeah, sure."

"And I wondered if, well, maybe I could take Hannah's diary with me."

I feel my stomach tighten at the idea of surrendering Hannah's diary. "But I'm not done yet," I say quietly.

"I know. But I think I need to read it, Kiera. I think I need it more than you do right now."

I actually agree with her, that she might need it more than I do. Even so, it's like surrendering my lifeline before getting safely to shore. Even if Mom is floundering out in the waves far beyond me, I don't want to hand it over.

"I think it'll help me get well," she says quietly.

"What if I make a copy of it?" I suddenly suggest. "In fact, that might be safer. You know, just in case you should misplace it or something at the rehab place. We really should keep her actual diary safe, don't you think? I don't even like taking it away from our house."

"Would you do that for me?" Her eyes grow big. "Make me my own copy?"

"Of course."

"And you won't leave any of it out?"

I suddenly remember about Max. "But there's some pretty hard stuff," I tell her. "Early on in the diary. It might upset you."

"I want everything there is," she says stubbornly. "Don't leave any of it out, Kiera."

"There are some missing pages—right in the part that's really hard. I'm sure Hannah tore them out herself." I don't really want to talk about this—and feel it will upset Mom. So I turn my focus to her rehab list. Besides listing what she needs to bring, it specifically lists what she cannot bring, including electronics, phones, and a few other things. "It says here that you can only bring *approved reading material*," I tell Mom. "What if they don't consider Hannah's diary approved reading material?"

"My own daughter's diary?" she questions. "Why wouldn't it be approved?"

"Well, you know how upsetting it was yesterday. Maybe they don't want you traumatized or hurt by something you read."

"But the truth is supposed to hurt, isn't it?"

"I guess…sometimes."

"So, you'll do it, Kiera? You'll make me my own copy?"

I nod. "But since I have to work tomorrow, I should probably try to figure this out today. There's a KopyKat nearby. How about I check to see if they're open?"

"Please, do that."

As I leave her room, I get an idea. Maybe I should make Dad a copy too. And maybe Grandma would appreciate one as well. And for Maddie. When she's older, I think she'll appreciate this. For some reason I feel like this could be the reason Hannah wrote so faithfully in her diary. Like maybe something inside of her knew she wouldn't be around for long, and she felt the need to document her life. Oh, I'm not saying she knew it was the last year of her life. But I can tell she was making the most of each day. A whole lot more than I've been doing. Hannah was living fully and asking God to use her—like she knew her days on earth were limited. I realize this sounds crazy and I don't plan to admit as much to anyone. But I feel like Hannah was running some sort of race against time—trying to pack as much as possible into each day.

When I call KopyKat, I discover they're open until five. I also discover it will not be cheap to make four copies of Hannah's diary. Still, I know it'll be worth it. So I call Dad and, without explaining all the details, get him to agree to pay for it—and to pick me up when I'm done. Then I spend the afternoon copying and assembling and binding, until I finally have four very decent looking copies of Hannah's diary tucked safely into my backpack. I call Dad, and he gives the clerk his credit card info then promises to pick me up later from the hospital.

I glance upward as I leave the store, hoping that Hannah is pleased with what I'm doing. Somehow I know that she is. Her diary has convinced me of how much she loves our family, and I believe her story can help us. But for the time being, it will only be Mom and me reading. I will stash the other copies away until the timing seems right.

I walk back to the hospital only to find Mom is too drowsy to talk coherently—and the nurse informs me she's had a dose of the meds they've given to help her through withdrawal. I write Mom a little note, saying I'll see her tomorrow, then kiss her cheek and go wait for Dad to pick me up. As I watch for his car, I consider giving him a copy of Hannah's diary now but decide against it. He just doesn't seem ready. Maybe after I've had a chance to read the whole thing myself, I'll feel more like giving it to him.

"Are you sure you'll be all right on your own?" Dad asks as he pulls into the driveway at our house. "I'm feeling kind of guilty for not moving back home with you while Mom's gone."

"It's okay," I assure him. "I'll be fine. Mostly I just go

to work then come home and crash. It's not like I have a life or a boyfriend or anything to worry you." I give him a sly grin.

Dad's brows arch. "What about that boy you brought to Larry's a few weeks ago? What's his name?"

"Bernard," I tell him. "He's just a friend and coworker. Don't worry."

Dad looks perplexed now. "Maybe this isn't such a good idea after all, Kiera."

I shrug. "Whatever. But I need to go in and start some laundry. My uniform never got washed last week and it—"

"Yeah, yeah." He waves me away. "I know you'll be fine. You were born sort of grownup. But you call me if you need anything. Or if you change your mind about being home alone. I can pack up and move back."

I put my backpack strap over a shoulder and roll my eyes, acting like I wouldn't like to accept his halfhearted offer. "I've pretty much been alone all summer, Dad. I honestly feel safer and more at peace with Mom gone than when she was here."

He nods sadly. "Yeah, I know what you mean."

"So don't worry. I'll be fine."

"Don't forget we activated the security system this morning," he reminds me. "I know we haven't used it much, but I want you to keep it—"

"I know, I know. You already reminded me a million times. Never mind that we live in the safest neighborhood in town." Except for me, I think as I close his car door. As I go up to the house, I cringe to remember the night I vandalized Max Harter's car. How could I have been so freaking crazy? What if I'd been caught? I felt somewhat silly after hearing Bernard's "investigative report." He was convinced that Max had changed a lot since high school, even claiming that Max claimed to have gotten religion. Well, I'm not so sure about that, and I still dislike the lowlife, but as I punch in the security code, I know that I've got more than enough on my plate right now. Max isn't worthy of my attention.

I dump my backpack in the kitchen then go start a load of laundry. It actually feels good to be home alone. I can make as much noise as I like. And leave messes wherever they land. I turn on my music—loud—then go scrounging for food in the kitchen. I remind myself of that kid in those old *Home Alone* movies—I even consider calling out for pizza but decide to try one of Mom's Lean Cuisine meals instead.

After dinner, I get out Mom's list for the rehab center and go about packing her Louis Vuitton bag. I'm determined to do a really good job, feeling kind of like a parent who's sending her kid off to sleepover camp for the first time, which is so strange. Although I wonder about the items she's penned at the bottom of the list—things like makeup and shampoo and moisturizer—I'm determined to make her happy. I start by putting the copy of Hannah's diary on the bottom of the bag, then raid her dresser for pajamas and underwear and socks. But as I search her closet for casual clothes like warm-ups and t-shirts and tennis shoes, I'm shocked by how much stuff she has. Really expensive stuff too—since a lot of it still has price tags. I don't know why she's never worn or used these things. So weird. So dysfunctional. I wonder if she could return some of it and get her money back. Wouldn't that help with her financial situation? Still, it's not my problem.

Finally, I get her bag filled with everything on the list—and then some. But now I realize I have a new problem. The Vuitton bag is too big to take on my bike. I suppose I could call Dad to come and get it for her. But then I get a better idea. I've really been missing Bernard these past few days. And I'm a little hurt that he never sent me beach pics. But I decide I'll ask him to give me a ride to the hospital tomorrow night. Might give us a chance to catch up.

Part of me feels embarrassed to have to admit to him that Mom's going to a drug rehab center. But then I realize he's heard most of my sad stories anyway. He won't be surprised. Besides, he's about the least judgmental person I know. Still, as I'm getting ready for bed, I think maybe I'm getting too old to be begging people for rides all the time. Maybe Dad's right. Maybe I should get my driver's license. Isn't that part of being grownup and independent?

Before I go to bed, I pull out Hannah's diary again. I've never actually read it in the house since that first time, but for some reason it's comforting to read it in my own room tonight. And her words of faith and hope and excitement for her future make me wonder if things could possibly get better for me. And honestly, it's hard to imagine how they could get much worse. Seriously, one sister is dead. One is probably never coming home again. My drug-addicted mom is going off for treatment—for who knows how long. My distracted dad has pretty much abandoned me. And yet, I don't feel too terrible. Just tired. Very tired.

Twenty-Five

IT'S SO GREAT TO GET BACK TO WORK. EVEN though I only had four days off, it feels like it's been a couple of weeks. And it's fun to realize how happy the kids are to see me again. As I interact with them, I remember Hannah's words about children. How much she loved them and wanted to help them. And it's so ironic that I'm working here. I'm pretty sure Hannah would approve.

Bernard seemed glad to see me too, but the day's been so crazy and busy, I've barely had a chance to talk to him. Finally, it's closing time and we're locking up the supply shed and shooing the kids home. "How was the beach?" I ask as I take out my backpack, waiting as he checks the door.

"Pretty good. Although it was kind of cool and foggy there. I guess that's typical this time of year."

"It was hot here," I say as I put straps over my shoulders. I still haven't told him anything about my holiday. As we head for the parking area, the last of the kids trickles away. "Can I ask you a favor?"

"Sure." He grins at me then nods toward his car. "But I can't give you a ride home. Maybe I should put a bike rack on the back."

I explain my dilemma about getting my mom's bag to the hospital.

"Your mom's in the hospital?" His dark eyes get big. "Is she okay?"

"Long story." I bend down to unlock my bike.

"Meaning you'll tell me if I give you a ride?" he teases.

I shrug as I shove my lock into my pack. "I'd tell you even if you didn't give me a ride, but I've got to get going if—"

"Of course, I'll give you a ride, Kiera. Want me to meet you at your house?"

"That'd be awesome."

"Want me to grab some Slurpees on my way?"

"That sounds *really* awesome." I hop on my bike. "I'll see if I can beat you."

"You're on."

Even though it's still pretty hot, I pedal hard with the hope of being rewarded with a Slurpee. Interestingly, we both arrive at almost the same time. I'm hot and sweaty and out of breath—but Bernard looks cool and calm. I invite him inside. "Give me a couple minutes," I call over my shoulder as I shoot upstairs. I rip off my park uniform and start to pull on some old cutoffs but then decide to wear something that won't upset my mom. Dressed somewhat respectably, I come down to find Bernard studying the photographs on the mantle in our living room.

"Nice looking family," he says as I drop Mom's Vuitton bag by the front door and pick up my Slurpee.

"We were, once upon a time." I go over to gaze at the photos too. Funny how they tell such a different story than what's really real. "Now...not so much."

"Ready?"

"Yeah. Thanks again for doing this."

As he drives to the hospital, I give him the short version of the past few days. He's so quiet, I wonder if I've shocked him. It is a lot to take in.

"Wow," he finally says. "You don't have an easy life, do you, Kiera?"

"I guess not. But it's probably not as bad as I make it sound."

"You seem to be handling it okay."

I shrug. Then, to change the subject, I tell him that I've decided to get my driver's license. "I'll need to practice driving some though. I haven't been behind a wheel for a while."

"Was that because of what happened to Hannah?"

"Not really. I had already decided that driving cars was environmentally irresponsible."

"Uh-huh?"

"I know I've been kind of extreme about a lot of things. I think it was my way of keeping people at bay. I mean, I do believe in protecting the environment—I don't plan to stop recycling or conserving. But I think it's okay to drive."

"That's good to know." Bernard chuckles. "So do you need some help with driving? I'm over eighteen. You can practice driving my car if you like."

"Really?"

"I guess I should find out your level of expertise before I make promises. You can drive, right?"

"Yes. I was a pretty good driver. But then I quit."

"Well, it's probably like riding a bike. You don't forget. You just need to brush up on your skills. And study for the test."

"I want to do that. And then I'll be able to drive my mom's car."

"Speaking of your mom, you'll need a parental signature to take your test." He offers to swing by the DMV to pick up an application. "That way you can get your mom to sign it today."

As I go in to get the application and a new manual, I'm so grateful for Bernard's friendship and help. I tell him so when I get back in the car. "I really appreciate it. You're as good as having a big brother."

He chuckles. "You seem different to me, Kiera."

"Different?"

"More level-headed. Not so angry."

"You thought I was angry?"

"I actually think you've got every right to be angry. But I'm glad to see that you're not. Anyway, not like you were before."

"Like when I was out vandalizing cars?" I tease.

He just shakes his head. "Hopefully you've put your juvenile delinquent days behind you now."

"I'm working on it."

"But seriously, the way you were talking about your mom just now. It's different. It's like you don't hate her anymore."

"Yeah, I guess I don't. I feel pretty sorry for her. She's a mess. But at least she's kind of admitting it now."

"And it's great she's getting rehab."

"Hopefully it'll stick." Although I'm sounding like my usual skeptic, I actually do feel hopeful. I think this is going to be a turning point for Mom. I tell Bernard about the diary and how I made her a copy.

"Are you worried about her reading the stuff about Max?"

"A little. But I think she has the right to know. And maybe the responsibility too."

"Uh, speaking of Max." He grimaces like this is uncomfortable.

"What about Max?"

"Well, I just found out that it wasn't his car that you vandalized."

"Of course, it was. I saw him driving it. We saw it in his driveway."

"Yeah, but I just learned it was his mom's car."

My stomach twists as Bernard turns into the hospital parking lot. "Are you serious?" I ask quietly.

"Yeah. I wasn't going to tell you…but maybe you need to know."

I let out a low groan as he pulls up to the front entrance. "Thanks. I mean, for the ride."

"Sorry, Kiera. I didn't want to make you feel horrible. You did what you did because of what Max did to your sister. I'm not saying that was right, but it's understandable."

"But stupid."

He shrugs. "So you want me to wait for you? I assume you'll need a ride home."

"You sure you want to give a ride to a criminal?"

His smile is my answer.

"I'd appreciate a ride," I confess. "But I need to talk to my mom for a while. You might not want to wait."

"I don't mind waiting for you. I'll park and meet you in the lobby waiting room."

"Thanks."

"I wish I hadn't mentioned that bit about Max. You probably didn't need that right now. I'm sorry."

"It's okay. I appreciate your honesty."

"Don't let it get to you." His eyes look concerned. "You

have a good heart, Kiera. I know that. And what you're doing for your mom right now proves it."

I thank him again as I pull out my mom's bag. As I walk into the hospital, I'm determined to do as he suggested. Put concerns about Max and all that behind me. It's comforting to know that Bernard still believes in me, and that he'll be waiting for me. My life is such a mess right now, who could blame him for leaving me in the dust?

I'm the only one in the elevator, just one more reminder of how alone I am in all this. Like I'm the only one Mom has to lean on right now. Sure, Dad tries to act supportive, and he did set up the rehab place. But he's still so disconnected. Like the invisible spouse. And I get it. It's entirely possible their marriage won't survive all this. But I wish it could. And despite what Mom says, I know she does too.

Mom looks genuinely glad to see me, but her eyes actually light up when she sees the Louis Vuitton bag. "Oh, thank you, Kiera. I was actually worried you'd bring my things in some old suitcase or even a garbage bag. I probably deserve that."

I roll my eyes. "Seriously?" I set her bag on a chair. "FYI, I packed very neatly—at least for me. And I think I got everything on your list. The copy of Hannah's diary is in the bottom."

Her smile fades slightly. "Thank you."

In an attempt to make small talk, I tell her that Bernard gave me a ride and even explain about his offer to help me get my license. "I decided it's time." I pull out the application and look around for a pen.

Her brow creases. "Are you sure?"

I firmly nod. "I need to do this."

"Well, it probably would make life simpler for everyone. And you could use my car while I'm, uh, gone. You know, to get groceries and things. Hopefully you won't go hot-rodding around." She signs the application and hands it back.

"Hot-rodding?" I snicker.

"Well, I trust you, Kiera. You've always been sensible. But I better tell you where to find my car key." She grimaces. "Hopefully you can." She sheepishly confesses to having lobbed it into the backyard. I don't even question this. I assume it was her attempt at self-preservation—or to avoid a DUI.

When it gets quiet again, I tell her about my day at the park and how happy the kids were to have us back there. I even tell her about Sheena and Sicily. "They're like poor little street urchins. Dirty and neglected, but sweet."

"Really?" She scowls. "Their parents don't care for them properly? That's terrible."

I explain a bit about the family's problems. "At first I blamed their neglect on the missing dad and then because the mom has a small baby. Now I'm not so sure."

"She sounds just plain lazy to me," Mom says a bit harshly.

"Or maybe she's depressed," I suggest.

"Yes, well, I suppose that could be. But a mother with young children doesn't really have the luxury of feeling depressed. She just has to do what needs to be done. That's what my grandmother and mother did. What I did." She frowns. "Well, what I used to do, when you girls were younger."

I consider this. "You did a great job at mothering when we were younger, Mom. We were always fed and clothed and supervised."

"Well, thank you." Her smile returns. "It's nice to hear you appreciated it."

I realize I might appreciate it more after having spent time with Sheena and Sicily. But I suppose I never really thought of it like that before. "I know you're going to get better," I tell her. "And I know you're going to be a good mom again. And hopefully a good wife too."

Her smile fades again. "I don't know. It feels like I'm about to go climb Mount Everest. In my bare feet."

"I think you can do it."

"I'll try."

We talk a while longer and I try to keep it upbeat, but finally I can tell she's tired. And I know Bernard is waiting. So I kiss her cheek and tell her good-bye.

Her eyes are misty as she looks up at me. "You've changed, Kiera."

"Is that good?" I ask.

"Yes." She nods. "But it's scary too."

"Scary?"

"I don't know how to explain it exactly… I guess it has to do with getting my hopes up. I'm afraid my expectations will be dashed. Both for you and for myself. That scares me."

"Oh." I know what she means. I could go back to my nasty, snarky self and start hurting everyone again. It's worried me too. "Well, maybe I'm growing up," I say brightly. "I suppose it's about time."

She looks uncertain. "Oh, you've always been growing up. I was just never sure what you were growing up to be."

"Well, I think Hannah is trying to help me."

Mom smiles again. "Maybe she can help both of us."

"I hope so." I tell her good-bye again then hurry out. I'm afraid I'm about to cry and don't want to upset her. But I do know what she means. It's like there's this high bar that we both want to get over, but neither of us is quite sure how to do it. All we can do is try.

Twenty-Six

AFTER A COUPLE DAYS OF SEARCHING, I find my mom's car key underneath the rhododendron bush in the backyard. And by the end of the week, after several practice runs with Bernard, I am the proud holder of an Oregon driver's license. Although Bernard heartily congratulates me, treating me to an ice cream cone to celebrate, he also feigns disappointment. At least I think it's an act. "So now you won't need me for rides anymore," he says as he drives me home on Friday afternoon.

"Don't be so sure about that. My mom is supposed to come home by mid-August. So I'll probably be back on my bike after that." Although it's nice to think he cares about this, I'm glad for this growing sense of independence. It's like being emancipated, only better. I have a place to live, a car to drive, and a job.

On Saturday morning, I make my first solo drive. It's only to the grocery store, but I feel strangely grownup as I load two bags of groceries in the back of my mom's car. And then I drive directly home. No hot-rodding.

My first week of living alone in our house proved so slovenly that even I am ashamed. Not to mention slightly disgusted. Really, is it necessary to be such a slob? And so I spend Saturday afternoon cleaning the whole house. And instead of feeling like an indentured servant, like I used to, I feel surprisingly empowered. And grownup.

After the house is clean, I settle down to read Hannah's diary. I've been reading some each evening. Now she's in late November. Her fundraiser is wrapped up, and she's thrilled that it was a huge success. And although I know she worked her tail off, she gives God all the credit. But the next entry is on the Friday after Thanksgiving and the first line catches me totally off guard.

> *I ran into Maxwell Harter tonight. He was home for Thanksgiving and showed up at homecoming. After I recovered from the shock of seeing him, I tried to act perfectly normal, but I couldn't figure out why he was going to such an effort to talk to me. Especially considering how I told him to never speak to me again last year. Still, I act civil.*
>
> *To my complete shock, Max took me aside in order to tell me that he's sorry. He admitted that*

he hurt me, took advantage of me, and probably deserved to be charged criminally. I was so stunned, I could barely respond. He continued by saying he was very sorry and that he hoped I would forgive him. "I have committed my life to Christ," he said with what seemed like sincerity. "And I've been convicted for what I did to you. I'm really, really sorry."

Well, I honestly can't remember exactly what I said to him. But I know I said I forgave him. That I had to forgive him because God, through Christ, has forgiven me. But I also told him that I was still scarred from it. And I told him he better never do that again to anyone else. He assured me he wouldn't. Then we parted ways.

Now that I'm home, still trying to wrap my head around that, I feel a strange sense of peace coming onto me. I think it's because, although I used to tell myself that I had forgiven him—because I knew after talking to Marnie I _needed_ to forgive him—I now realized that I finally _have_ forgiven him. And the reason I felt peace was because for the first time, I was free from him. By forgiving him, I had freed myself from the pain of remembering what he'd done. Oh, I'm sure I'll still have to deal with stuff related to that. But for the most part, I feel sort of okay about it. I never really *thought I'd feel free like this, but I do. And I know it's only because of God.*

And I'm really thankful that God has managed to salvage Max's life. Oh, I never want to be involved with him again. But for Max's sake, I'm glad. I'm praying that God will lead and direct him from now on. And hopefully God will take what could've been used for evil and use it for good. Because miracles do happen. I'm sure I witnessed one tonight. Praise God!

As I close Hannah's diary, I don't know what to think. Or how to feel. Besides being reminded of my guilt over Max's mother's car, I feel confused, and slightly angry. Even though Bernard told me that Max had changed, I didn't want to believe it. How can someone that evil turn it around? I've been determined to hate Max Harter until the end of time—end of story. Now I don't know what to do or how to react. And what if Hannah was simply being naïve? About to be taken in? Although it's reassuring that she says she'd never get involved with him again.

But how could she forgive him so easily? And I know she wasn't making that up. Hannah has always been very honest in her diary. So even if I believe she truly did forgive him—I just can't imagine how. It seems humanly impossible. In fact, I must agree with her last line. It does seem miraculous. Flat out miraculous. I doubt I'll ever be able to forgive like that.

And I wish the car had belonged to Max—that way I wouldn't feel so guilty.

After her first week in rehab, Moira felt completely and thoroughly humiliated. Okay, maybe the more accurate word was humbled. At least that's what her counselor called it. But it felt more like intentional humiliation to Moira. Their way of breaking people. Knock them down to size so you can fix them. Sort of like a concentration camp. At least that was how it felt at first.

For starters she'd been outraged and indignant when the intake counselor had not only searched her, but gone all through her Louis Vuitton bag, removing "contraband" items like makeup and personal toiletries. Really? Did they think she'd hidden drugs inside her expensive skin care products? But the worst part was when the woman confiscated the photocopied diary, acting as if it might be dangerous.

"Why can't I have that?" Moira had demanded. "That happens to be my dead daughter's diary and I wanted to—"

"Your counselor has to approve it," the woman had declared with no mercy.

Then to add insult to injury, Moira had to share a room. And it wasn't even a very big room. Her roommate was a young meth addict who'd been there a couple of weeks. To be more correct, Sybil was a *recovering* meth addict.

And to be fair, she was actually quite sweet, but the tattoos and piercings had been disturbing. Moira had woken in the middle of her first night there, certain that Sybil was a psycho and about to murder her.

But Moira slowly got used to Sybil's appearance. Still it troubled her, as a mother, because she still harbored deep fears that Kiera might do something like that to herself. She'd asked for permission to get a tattoo last year. Naturally Moira had put her foot down. But it was possible that Kiera was out there right now, driving Moira's car to tattoo parlors and possibly getting various body parts pieced as well. And there was nothing Moira could do about it.

The next part of her humiliation was being the oldest person in rehab. Even her counselor was younger. But Lacey had the right credentials, and she was kind but firm. Lacey assured Moira that their center had experience with older patients, but for now it was Moira and a bunch of twenty- and thirty-somethings. The upside was that these younger residents tended to leave Moira alone. Well, until the group therapy sessions. Then, if she said anything that sounded the least bit "uppity" they were quick to call her on it. And they didn't let her get away with playing the "pity card" either. Oh, they listened to her excuses—once. After that they forced her to own her addiction. Although it was humiliating, she knew it was probably good.

By the second week, Moira felt a bit more settled in the rehab center's routines. She no longer resented being awakened so early, or the forced exercise routine, or the mandatory chores, or even the institutionalized food. Sure, it was a lot like being incarcerated, but she knew she deserved it. She still bristled at the transparency of the group sessions, but she did appreciate her private counseling with Lacey. For the first time in her life, she felt like she was being completely honest. There was no point in trying to maintain her perfect façade here. And so she completely let her hair down, without fear of judgment. And it was strangely liberating.

"I think you're ready to read your daughter's diary now," Lacey told Moira on her tenth day there.

"Really?" Moira felt hopeful.

"Yes. I think it will actually be healthy for you, to help you to deal with your loss." She slid the photocopied book across her desk. "I read parts of it myself, and your daughter seems a very sensible and sensitive young woman."

Moira nodded solemnly. "She was an amazing girl."

"Well, I'd like you to read it—and bring it with you for our sessions. We can talk about it together."

"Thank you." Moira clutched the book to her chest. Part of her was excited about reading Hannah's words— another part of her was terrified. She knew it would be painful. Perhaps even more than she could bear. But at least it wouldn't drive her to pills and booze, since that wasn't an option here.

After being home alone for two weeks, the novelty has worn off. It's Saturday afternoon, and although I've done my Saturday morning routine of grownup chores, I'm now feeling lonely and don't know what to do about it. I know that Dad's golfing as usual. And Bernard told me he was needed at the tire store. Not that he'd want to hang with me anyway…but I like to imagine he would.

Although I haven't opened it since reading about Hannah's post-Thanksgiving encounter with Max, I'm tempted to pull out Hannah's diary again. That's how lonely I feel at the moment. But when I open the small blue book to where I marked it with a slip of paper, I realize that the next entry to read is in December. It's unsettling to see that this is Hannah's final month. I close the book and take a deep breath.

I'm not sure I can even take it right now. Not when I'm already feeling so lonely. I suddenly miss Hannah so much that it literally aches deep inside my chest. I feel that, if she were here, I could probably talk to her in a way that we never talked before. I feel like she could understand me in a way that no one else ever has. But she's not here! She is gone. *Too soon.*

It makes me want to shake my fist at God—I want to demand to know why he took her away like that. Doesn't he understand that it was too soon? Doesn't he get how much I need her in my life—right now? Why? Why? Why?

Instead of holding them back, I let the tears flow freely. I allow myself to walk around my house just wailing and crying—truly grieving for what I lost when my sister died. Something I've never fully done before. I even go into her room…and just lie there on her bed…sobbing and sobbing…until there are no more tears.

I sit up and look around. Instead of feeling critical of the sweet space she created or wanting to take pokes at her shabby chic creativity, I realize how comforting this room feels. So much more so than my own stark room that's usually a mess, but cleaner than usual now. And, not feeling like an intruder, but almost like an invited guest, I start poking around. I read various cards that are in an old cigar box that she decorated with buttons and lace. I'm surprised that several cards are from Hannah's youth pastor friend Marnie. I guess they were closer than I realized. Certainly Marnie was closer to my sister than I was. I try not to feel resentful…but I do.

I notice Hannah's Bible by her bedside. It's relatively new. She must've gotten it after her "coming to faith" experience at that weekend camp. I absently flip it open and am surprised to see that it's inscribed by Marnie. So it must've been a gift. There's also a reference to what I assume is a Bible verse, which I decide to look up. John 3:16. Almost like it could hold some sort of clue. Despite my years of attending church as a child, I'm not really familiar with the Bible, and it takes me awhile to locate the book of John. But when I do, I'm surprised to see the lines I'm looking for are highlighted in yellow. In fact, I noticed a lot of lines are highlighted and there are even some handwritten notes in the margin. I'm surprised Hannah thought it was okay to mark up a Bible like that.

> *God loved the people of this world so much that he gave his only Son, so that everyone who has faith in him will have eternal life and never really die.*

I stare at those words for a long time and then reread them, aloud this time. Trying to wrap my head around the meaning. Of course, I have no doubts that my sister believed those lines wholeheartedly. And if those words are really true, that would mean she's still alive. Not that it does me any good, since she's not here. Still, I suppose it would be a comfort to think she is still alive…somewhere. I close the Bible and set it back on her bedside table, exactly where it was because I can see the rectangular shape framed by a thin layer of dust. My mom has obviously not been up here to clean for quite a while.

I suddenly find myself obsessing over the mysterious Marnie. Oh, she's not really that mysterious. I've met her before. Once when Hannah was alive and then at the memorial service. Marnie was pretty and polite and, like everyone else, upset over Hannah's death.

The frustrating part about Marnie is simply that I don't know her. And it's hard to admit it, but I resent that Hannah was so close to her. And I resent that Marnie signed everything to Hannah with "your sister in Christ." Almost like she was trying to replace me. And yet I know that I was a hopeless excuse of a sister. Who could blame Hannah for looking elsewhere? But it hurts.

I now have an irrepressible urge to talk to Marnie. But I don't even know her last name. I know her husband's name is Kent and they have a couple of kids. But I really don't know how to get in contact with them. That's when I notice Hannah's favorite bag hanging on the back of her door, just like it always did...only a little more beat up than I recall. Then I remember—it was probably with her on the night of the wreck. And my mom probably cleaned it up and hung it there.

I open the bag and am surprised to see that all of Hannah's usual things are inside—including her smart phone. Almost like she plans to use it again. It doesn't take long to locate her charger and plug in the phone. After a couple minutes, it starts to come to life. I quickly find Marnie's phone number, and the next thing I know I'm calling her on my phone—with no idea of what I plan to say.

And then she says, "Hello?"

"I—I'm sorry to call you out of the blue," I stammer. "But I'm Hannah Josephson's sister and I—I just wanted to talk to you."

"Kiera," she says warmly, as if she actually knows me. "I've always hoped you would call. How are you doing?"

"Not—not so well," I nervously confess.

"Do you want to talk?"

Her tone is so genuine, so inviting… I admit that I *do* want to talk. Marnie explains she was about to go run some errands. "So Kent is watching the kids. I can meet you somewhere. Or I could just stop by your house, it's on the way."

"Yes," I say eagerly. "That'd be great if you could come here." After I hang up, I wonder what I've gotten myself into. What on earth am I going to say to her? After all, she's a complete stranger. And yet…she was so close to Hannah.

Twenty-Seven

BY THE TIME MARNIE ARRIVES, I FEEL LIKE
every nerve ending is lying outside of my skin. I try to act
calm as I let her inside the house. As I lead her to the living
room, I'm trying to hold back my tears, wondering how I
can possibly have any left. But Marnie seems completely
at ease as we sit down. Like nothing about this meeting is
unusual.

"I feel like I know you, Kiera," she says gently. "Hannah loved you so much. She was always talking about
you."

"Seriously?" I frown. "I was so awful to her. So mean."

Marnie has a faint smile. "Yes, but Hannah understood."

"Understood?"

"Hannah knew that *hurt* people *hurt* people."

"Oh…" I make a sheepish nod as the words sink in. "I guess that's true."

"Anyway, she was always praying for you. And so were we. We still do."

I don't know how to respond to that. Don't even know why I asked her to come. Almost wishing I hadn't. This will probably just prolong my pain.

"I miss Hannah so much." She sighs. "I'm sure you do too."

"Yeah." To my surprise, I confess about reading her diary.

"That's right. I remember she told me she kept a diary."

"I don't know how much you knew about what happened to her… Specifically, I mean, with Max."

Marnie nods solemnly. "Yeah, she told me all about it. That was a tough one. I wanted her to go to the police, but she refused. Kent and I went round and round about the whole thing. We wanted to report what had happened, but Hannah begged us not to. She said she couldn't bear it. Finally, Kent agreed to make it his mission to work on Max. He met with him and told him that we knew everything—and that we'd be keeping an eye on him. To Kent's surprise, Max asked to meet with him again…and again."

"Maybe he was afraid that you guys would report him if he didn't."

"It was more than that, Kiera. Max was carrying a load of guilt. He admitted he'd taken advantage of Hannah that night—and that she was impaired. But he wasn't the one to slip her the roofie. A buddy of his at the party did it—thought it would be funny."

"Real funny."

"Well, he actually liked Hannah. But after that night she wouldn't give him the time of day. When he found out his friend had doped her drink, Max felt even worse, but he didn't know what to do about it . . . how to make it right."

"It's not like he could undo the damage."

Marnie nodded. "Anyway, he continued to meet with Kent and eventually made a commitment to Christ."

"That must've been when he tried to make things right with Hannah." I still feel skeptical. What if it was all just an act?

"Max was devastated when he heard about Hannah's death. He came straight to us—and he was a mess."

"Oh?"

"I think that impacted him more than anything. He's a different guy now. Night and day different."

"So that's how Max changed." I feel myself stumbling over the words. It's like they taste all wrong in my mouth. Especially when talking about the monster who hurt my sister.

"Yeah. He's still getting over his guilt and grief over Hannah, and he's met with Kent a couple of times this summer. But it sounds like he's leaning on God more than ever, growing stronger in his faith."

"Oh."

"Was that what you wanted to talk about today?" Marnie's brow creases slightly.

"I don't know."

Marnie leans forward, peering intently at me. "How are you *really* doing, Kiera?"

I feel the tears burning behind my eyelids again, the lump growing in my throat. I'm tempted to confess that my family is a great big dysfunctional mess and that my parents are splitting and my mom's in rehab... But that really isn't the worst of my problems.

"I just feel so guilty," I blurt out. "I'm mad at God for taking Hannah away. But I'm more mad at myself."

"Why?" she asks gently.

"Because it's my fault that Hannah died that night."

"How can it possibly be your fault?" Marnie asks in a firmer tone.

"Because I called home that night. On New Year's Eve." Tears are coming as the words pour out. "Dad took me to the sleepover at Lana's house. I didn't want to go, but Dad thought it was good for me because I hadn't been getting along with my friends. He thought it would fix everything, and he promised me that he'd come get me if it fell apart. But Lana had told me it would be okay. Then Meg got all mean and nasty. And I called home—" I can't talk anymore because the tears are choking me.

Marnie comes to sit next to me on the couch, putting an arm around my shoulders. "It's not your fault, Kiera," she says when I finally stop sobbing. "You can't blame your-self."

"But Hannah was driving that night—because of me."

"So are you responsible for the ice on the road that night?" she asks with an intensity that catches me off guard. "And are you responsible for the tree growing alongside the road? And what about Hannah's car, are you responsible for the way it was built—with no engine in front to absorb the crash? And what about the timing of the car that Hannah swerved to miss? Are you responsible for that too? Are you claiming responsibility for all those things, Kiera? Because if you are, then you are saying you're God. And you're not God, are you?"

Those words sound familiar—and I'm suddenly reminded of the old woman at the hospital. "No," I say quietly. "I'm not God. But are you saying it's God's fault that Hannah is dead?"

"First of all, I don't believe Hannah *is* dead. I believe she's more alive than she ever was here on earth. And happier too. But I also believe that God could've prevented Hannah's accident that night…if he'd wanted to."

"Why didn't he want to?" I demand. "Why did he have to take her so soon?"

"I don't know why, Kiera. And I'll admit that I wasn't a big fan of it either. I miss her too. There are a lot of things about God that I don't understand yet. But I believe this— God knows what he's doing, and he knows what's best for us. We are so limited with these earth-eyes. We only see here and now. God sees *everything*. Heaven and earth, yesterday, today, and forever. He doesn't separate earthly life from heavenly life. He's not limited like that. To God it's all one big, beautiful thing. Hannah could be here or Hannah could be there—but she's still alive. And I believe that God brings vast good out of what seems bad."

Even though I don't understand much of what she just said, I think I get some of it—kind of like a tiny glimmer of light in a long dark tunnel. "So you honestly believe that Hannah is still alive? That she is with God?"

"Absolutely. One-hundred percent."

"I wish I could believe that."

"It takes faith, Kiera. And faith is a gift from God. We don't come by it naturally. We have to ask God to help us with it."

"Oh."

"Can I pray with you? I realize you might not believe in prayer, but I do. And if you don't mind, I'd like to pray with you."

I don't refuse, but most of her words seem to float right over my head. Still, I feel oddly comforted when she is done. "Thanks," I tell her. "You've given me a lot to think about."

"Will you call me again when you need to talk?" she asks hopefully as I walk her to the front door.

"Do you want me to?"

"Of course." Her face lights up with a big smile. "In fact, I'd love to have you come visit us, Kiera." She holds up her phone. "And I've got your number now. So how about next week? We'll have you over for dinner. You can come early and help with the kids while I get it ready. Okay?"

"Okay."

"I'll call with the details." Marnie hugs me, holding me tightly like she really means it. "I'm so glad you called me. I know we're going to be good friends." And, just like that, she leaves.

Not only do I finish reading Hannah's diary that same day, I start to read it again—from the beginning the next morning. And with what feels like a new set of eyes. As I read, I'm so touched by Hannah's deep love for our family that it makes me want to reach out to them…on Hannah's behalf.

I start by calling Maddie, waiting until I'm sure that she and Grandma are home from church. Although Maddie and I have exchanged several texts, I haven't actually spoken to her since she left, and I'm shocked at how happy she is to talk to me. "I miss you so much, Kiera! I'm having fun here, but I wish you were here too."

I explain that my job's keeping me pretty busy and attempt to make encouraging small talk, trying hard not to mention anything about our parents' ongoing dilemmas. "I just really wanted to hear your voice," I tell Maddie. "I'm so glad you're having a good time and doing well." Now there's a long pause and for some reason I suspect something's amiss. "Maddie, are you still there?"

"Yes. I just wanted to go outside to talk. Can I, uh, can I tell you something, Kiera?"

"Of course. You can tell me anything."

"It's a secret. I've been keeping it for a while. But I just feel like I can't keep it anymore. It feels like I can't breathe sometimes. And I don't mean because of asthma or allergies or anything."

"What is it?" I try to sound more gentle than eager, but my heart is pounding. What is wrong with my baby sister? Is she sick?

"It's about Hannah," she says quietly.

"Okay. You can tell me anything you want about her, Maddie. I've actually been thinking about Hannah a lot this summer. I mean really a lot."

"And you know it's her birthday soon. Just two weeks."

"Yeah, I know." I also know that's about when Mom is supposed to come home from rehab. I'm trying not to think about how that will go—if she'll relapse because of it. "Is that what your secret is about? Hannah's birthday?"

"No, no, that's not it. But I was just thinking about that today. Her birthday, I mean. No, the secret is something really terrible, Kiera. Something I've never told anyone. Not Mom or Dad or anyone."

"Go ahead," I urge her. "You can tell me. I'm your sister."

"Okay." She makes a loud sigh. "It's about Hannah. You remember that day—on New Year's Eve. You were going to the sleepover, but you didn't really want to go. But Dad thought you should go? Remember?"

"Yes, I totally remember that."

"So, anyway, Dad took you over to Lana's. And while you guys were gone, Hannah asked me to go to the New Year's Eve service with her and—" Maddie's voice breaks and now she's crying. "And I—I told her *no*. I said I didn't want to go. I told her it was because I was tired and it would be too late—and the truth is I just wanted to finish the book I was reading and—and—"

"But that's okay, Maddie. I'm sure Hannah understood."

"But if I'd said yes that night, if I'd gone with her, she wouldn't have been able to go pick you up, Kiera. We would've still been at the church service. And she—she would still be alive. Don't you get it? It's *my* fault that Hannah died!" And now Maddie is sobbing hard, and I feel so awful for her—and so far away.

"Maddie," I say slowly but loudly. "Maddie, listen to me, okay?"

"O-okay," she sobs. "I—I'll try."

"It is not your fault that Hannah died."

"But it *is* my fault. I should've said yes and—"

"Then I would have to say it's *my* fault, Maddie. I'm the one who called for a ride that night. If I hadn't wanted to come home, Hannah would be alive."

"But I—"

"Listen to me, Maddie. We can all blame ourselves if

we want to, but someone just told me something. In fact, two people told me almost the exact same thing. If we blame ourselves, it's like saying *we are God*. It's like saying we had control over everything that went on that night." Now I repeat almost verbatim what Marnie told me about the icy road and tree and other car. "Did you arrange all those things, Maddie?"

"No...."

"Neither did I. We can't blame ourselves for something we had no control over."

"But I just wish I'd gone to church with her."

"What if you had, Maddie? What if both you and Hannah had been killed that night? Would that make anything better?"

There's a brief silence. "No...I guess not."

Now I confess that I've been reading Hannah's diary.

"You're kidding!" Maddie sounds understandably shocked.

"I think she wanted me to read it, Maddie. And I made copies for everyone. For Mom and Dad and you and Grandma too. I think we all need to read it to understand Hannah better. And to understand how much she loves us." And then I promise to mail them tomorrow—a copy for Maddie, and one for Grandma. Of course, I'll make sure that Maddie gets the one not containing the part about Max. She's not ready for that. Maddie thanks me and then has to cut the call short because Kendall is calling for her.

"You and Kendall have fun," I say. "And no more blaming yourself for something you had no control over. You're not God, Maddie."

"Okay. Thanks, Kiera."

As I hang up, I feel like Hannah would approve. Maybe I don't fully believe everything I just said to her, but I'd like to believe it…maybe I'm working on believing it. Now I know I need to give Dad his copy of Hannah's diary too. Without calling him, I drive over to his apartment complex. I've only been there once, but I was surprised at how nice it was. To me it didn't look like a temporary setup. It looked like he had moved out for good. And it made me mad. I knock on his door and, when he doesn't answer, I assume he's playing golf or hanging with one of his buddies. So I slip the copy of Hannah's diary under his doormat and just go. Hopefully he'll see it there. And I'm kind of glad that he doesn't know I'm the one who brought it over. Might give him something to think about! Like his daughter talking to him from beyond the grave. I can only hope so.

Twenty-Eight

ON MONDAY NIGHT, AFTER MAILING THE package to my grandma's house, I keep a close watch on my phone, expecting Dad to call me about the parcel I left on his doorstep. When he doesn't call, I feel aggravated. Even so, I refuse to give him the satisfaction of me calling him first. I just hope he actually got the photocopied diary. I'd hate to think it wound up in someone else's hands. In that case, I might not even want him to know.

On Tuesday, after work, Bernard suggests a trip to the lake to cool off. We're having another heat wave this week, so I eagerly agree. First we jump in the lake and enjoy a good swim, then we rent kayaks for a while, and finish it off by having hotdogs from the food trailer. All in all, it's a perfect evening. And, unless I'm imagining things, it's almost like a date. But, thankfully, we do not kiss afterward. I am not ready for that. But as we sit in his car in my driveway, we do talk about the summer coming to an end. He returns to college in two weeks, and I'm touched when he asks if we can remain in touch. Naturally, I say yes.

On Wednesday, my mom leaves a message during the day. She apologetically explains that it's family night at her rehab center tonight, inviting me to come visit her. The center is about an hour drive, but I decide to go anyway. It feels awkward to go through the security guard—like this is a prison. And it's weird seeing my mom in a place like that, surrounded by a bunch of recovering addicts and looking strange with no makeup and her hair pulled tightly back, with gray roots showing. But she actually seems okay. Kind of a raw and worn-out sort of okay, but she seems happy to see me.

We all sit together, family style, and have a dinner that's not very appetizing, then we watch a video and listen to a guy talking about how important it is for family to be supportive without being codependent. Okay, I get that. Afterward, Mom asks me to take a walk outside with her and before long we're sitting on a bench beneath a shady tree.

"I read all of Hannah's diary," she tells me. "It wasn't easy…but I read the whole thing."

"Were you shocked about what happened with Max?"

She nods with wide eyes. "I had no idea. She never said a word to me."

"She was good at hiding her pain behind that happy face."

"I feel like I failed her, Kiera."

"I feel like we *all* failed her."

"Not like I did." Mom sighs. "I've been talking to Lacey about it."

"Lacey?"

"My counselor. It helps to talk about it, but I still feel very guilty."

"Guilty?"

Mom holds up her hands, and I notice how short and ragged her nails are, almost as if she's been chewing on them. "I was so negligent. Not just of Hannah. But all of you. I've been such a failure as a mom."

"But you're working on it."

"There's more, Kiera." Mom looks at me with troubled eyes. "I feel that I'm to blame for her death. I know I've tried to blame everyone else. Your dad and grandma over that car. And you for needing a ride. But it's all just been a cover-up for my own responsibilities. Lacey has helped me to recognize that."

"What do you think your responsibilities are?"

"That night. New Year's Eve. You were at the sleepover when your dad and I got into a big fight. I wanted him to take me out somewhere. I'd gotten all dressed up and everything. But he didn't want to go anywhere. So we fought about it."

"Yeah?" I want to ask what was new about that—hadn't they been fighting a lot the past couple of years?

"Anyway, I opened a bottle of wine…and your dad went to bed. When you called, I should've gone to get you, but I'd been drinking and didn't think that was a good idea. And your dad was asleep. So I let Hannah go. And instead of telling her to take my car—since I should've known it would be icy out—I never said a word." Mom's eyes are overflowing with tears now. "So, you see, I'm to blame."

To my surprised amazement, I'm now repeating the same thing I told Maddie—the thing that Marnie told me—to my mother. "So," I finish it off, "that's like saying you're God—like you have control over everything."

She stares at me with wonder. "I didn't know you had such strong faith, Kiera."

"Well, I wouldn't call it strong faith. But I guess I'm working on it. Reading Hannah's diary has helped a lot. I'm actually reading it again." Now I tell her about talking to Maddie. I don't go into all the details about Maddie's "secret," but I do admit that I've sent copies—an edited one for Maddie and one for Grandma. "And I gave one to Dad too."

"What did he say?"

I shrug. "I haven't heard from him."

"Figures." She shakes her head. "I haven't heard from him either."

I try not to show how aggravated this makes me, but

seeing that it's getting late and I still have an hour's drive, I tell Mom good-bye and am surprised that she hugs me.

"Thanks for coming, Kiera." She looks into my eyes. "And thanks for being such a good daughter. I don't know what I'd do without you."

I try not to act shocked by this, but tell her to take care and keep getting better. "And feel free to invite me to family night again," I say as we go back inside. "It's kind of interesting."

Mom sort of laughs. "Interesting is one word for it."

As I drive home, I try to imagine what it must feel like for Mom to be there. It's so unlike anything she's used to. I'm actually impressed that she hasn't thrown a hissy fit and demanded to be released. Dad told me she could do that. He even predicted she would.

On Thursday, I go to Marnie and Kent's after work. First I hang out with Marnie and the kids outside. She's set up a small wading pool, and the kids are really into it. Then I help with them and with dinner and by the end of the evening, I honestly feel almost like family. They're all so comfortable and easy to be with. I think I understand why Hannah spent so much time over here. And when Kent asks me to come to their Bible study on Saturday night, I actually agree. Okay, as I drive home, I'm already thinking of excuses not to go, but there's a small chance I will.

On Friday, as I'm driving home from work, I'm seriously aggravated that Dad hasn't called me—so much so that I'm thinking I'll just break down and call him and demand to know what's up. But to my surprise, his car is just pulling up into our driveway as I get there.

"You're driving?" He says with a worried look. "Your mom's car too?"

"Yeah." I jingle the keys in front of him. "She said it's okay."

"But your license?"

"I got it," I tell him proudly.

He looks shocked. "Wow. You're just full of surprises."

I'm leading the way up to the house, unlocking the door and disarming the system with a new pass code that I recently installed. Probably to teach my dad a lesson just in case he decided to drop by when I wasn't home.

I toss my backpack on the foot of the stairs then go to the fridge for a soda. "What are you doing here?" I ask with slight irritation.

"Well, this is still my house," he says a bit indignantly. "At least I pay the bills for it."

"Oh, yeah. But you don't live here," I remind him as I pop open the can. "But help yourself to a drink if you like."

"Thanks, I will."

I sit down at the breakfast bar, watching as he opens the fridge, giving it a good long look before removing a Sierra Mist. "Looks like your housekeeping skills have improved, Kiera."

"I guess that comes from living alone. No one to blame

for anything but myself. As it turns out, I kind of like a clean house."

Dad chuckles and sits across from me. "Okay, I can tell you're mad at me. Mind telling me why?"

"Hmm…where to begin?"

Dad frowns. "So you have a whole list?"

"First of all, I'm mad at you for ignoring Mom. I went to see her this week. For family night. She said she hasn't heard a word from you. Not in the hospital. Not at the rehab center. I don't get that. I mean, you married her, Dad. I assume your vows were for 'better or worse' and 'richer or poorer' and 'in sickness and health.' Well, sure, she's been sick. And maybe there's been more worse than better. But it looks like you're just bailing on her, which brings me to another thing. I'm irritated at you for getting that apartment—like you've completely given up on your marriage. Even though Mom is actually trying to get clean. And then I'm mad at you for completely neglecting Maddie and me." I shake a finger at him. "You're actually worse than Mom about that. I mean at least she had an excuse. But you just choose to go your own way, because you're just plain selfish. And finally, I'm mad at you for ignoring the fact that I left a pretty important thing on your doorstep last Sunday."

"Wow." He shakes his head. "That's quite a list."

"Well, you asked." I take a long sip then wipe the can across my forehead.

Dad lets out a slow sigh. "Okay, you're right about me

sort of bailing on your mom. I mean, she did tell me to go, but she was under the influence at the time. So maybe that wasn't really fair. But the fact of the matter is that our marriage has had problems. And the problems didn't start with Hannah's death either. That just seemed to shine a giant spotlight on everything that was already wrong."

I nod. "Yeah, I get that. Reading Hannah's diary actually helped me to understand that better. Apparently she could see it long before anyone else."

He slowly shakes his head. "Yeah, I had no idea she was aware of all that."

"So you've been reading it?"

He nods sadly. "Yeah. And it hasn't been easy. I'm still not done with it."

"It's not easy for any of us," I point out. Then I tell him how I've given copies to everyone. "Maddie's was edited for her age," I explain. "But she needs to read it as much as any of us. Even if it's not easy."

Dad looks so sad now that I wonder if he's about to cry. And I'm not sure I can take it. I only saw him cry once before—when Hannah died. "You're right that I've neglected you and Maddie," he confesses. "And it seems I neglected Hannah too. Although there's not much I can do about that now."

"There might be."

"What do you mean?"

"I mean that Hannah wanted us to change, Dad. She wanted all of us to change. Didn't you read that prayer she wrote on New Year's Eve?" I feel the lump in my throat to remember her words. "She prayed that something would shake us and wake us up—so that we'd look up and see God."

"Do you think that's why she died?" Dad's eyes look seriously misty.

"I don't know. But I think God is using her death to get to us. And if we want to honor Hannah's memory—and help her prayers to get answered—I think we should allow her death to change us. I know it's changing me."

He runs a hand through his hair and lets out another loud sigh. "It's always just been easier to ignore everything. When I realized I couldn't fix this family, I just got busy with other things. I'll admit it. If I can lose myself in work and golf and ESPN or whatever, that's what I want to do. It's easier than feeling so much pain."

"And that's what Mom was doing too. Losing herself in shopping. Then booze and, after Hannah died, she added pills to the mix."

"But I still don't know how to fix this, Kiera." Dad looks slightly desperate now. "I really don't. It's easier to just walk away."

"Is easier better?"

"No." He sighed. "Of course not."

"You haven't even asked how Mom is doing."

"How is she?"

"I think she's getting better."

"Good."

"Why don't you go see her? Or call or write her a letter or something."

"I'll think about it."

"You know she comes home just before Hannah's birthday."

Dad rolls his eyes. "Great timing, huh?"

"Maybe." Now I decide to throw something at him… something I've been thinking about. "I want to have a birthday party for Hannah."

"What?" He looks truly alarmed.

"Okay, not a birthday party. But I want to have our whole family together on her birthday. It's just over a week away. On Sunday. I think it would be like a gift to her if we could all get together. Even if it's just for one day."

"I don't know…."

"Well, fine. If you don't want to come—*fine!* But I'm asking everyone else. I'm going to ask Grandma to bring Maddie home that weekend. It's just a week until school starts and—"

"But Maddie might go to school there—and stay with Grandma."

"What if Maddie doesn't want to stay with Grandma? You can't just blow this family apart because it's convenient for you, Dad."

"I'm not doing that."

"Well, it seems like you're awfully eager to give up."

"I just feel caught between a rock and a hard place."

"Maybe you should finish reading Hannah's diary," I challenge him. "In fact, that will be a prerequisite. In order to come for Hannah's birthday. We all have to read her whole diary. I'm sure Maddie will have no problem with that. She's probably already finished it."

Dad scowls. "Who said you can call the shots?"

I hold up my hands and look around the kitchen. "This is what happens when you leave your kid home alone, Dad. She starts to rule the roost. If you don't like it, do something about it. In the meantime, why don't you finish reading your dead daughter's diary."

Dad gets a hard look in his eyes now. "What about that thing that happened with Max Harter? Shouldn't we do something about that? It's wrong for a criminal to walk around free—after doing what he did. If I could get my hands on the—"

"Dad!" I wave my hand in front of his face to get his attention. "I actually know exactly how you feel."

"Exactly how I feel?" His scowl is skeptical. "I doubt that."

"Would you like to hear what I did to Max?"

"Huh?"

So, even though I never planned to tell another living soul, I am now confessing to Dad about the night I sent Nora that anonymous note and then stenciled Max's car.

Dad's brows are raised high in alarm. "With permanent paint?"

"Yep." Now I sheepishly admit what I later learned,

both from Bernard and Marnie, about Max changing. "And Hannah even wrote about it in her diary. But not until much later. If you'd read the whole thing, you'd know it too."

Dad looks truly flustered. "I don't know what to say. Clearly, I've been a little checked out in the parenting department."

"Hey, it's not too late. You still have two kids." I weigh my words now. "And even if your marriage is unfixable, Dad, you owe it to Mom to talk to her about it."

He sets down his soda can. "Well, you've given me plenty to think about, Kiera."

I shrug. "You asked."

"I guess I have some reading to catch up on this weekend." He pulls out his wallet, laying some bills on the table. "I'll add a little extra for your, uh, birthday party...or whatever you're calling it."

"Then you'll come?" I ask hopefully.

"We'll see."

After Dad leaves, I wonder if I just bit off more than I can chew. A birthday party for my dead sister? Who does that? But I'm resolved to pull it off. And so I start making invitations. One to send to my mom's rehab place and one for Grandma and Maddie, which I plan to follow up with a phone call. I want Maddie to know it's okay to come home—if she wants to. I hope she'll want to. And, as a reminder for Dad, I decide to make one for him too. Hopefully he'll come.

Twenty-Nine

BERNARD HELPS KEEP ME SANE IN THE DAYS before my mom's stint in rehab comes to an end. We spend almost every evening after work together. And I'm getting the feeling that it's more than just a friendship too. Still, I don't want to push things—and I'm relieved he's not. We still have one last week of working at the park—and lots of fun activities to keep us on our toes with the kids. Not to mention that Val is bringing a video crew with her to document how great this program has been working. So, for now, I'm just thankful that Bernard is such a good friend. If that changes later…maybe even after he goes back to school…well, fine.

Right now, as I'm driving to pick up my mom from rehab on Saturday afternoon, I'm mostly concerned about the state of my fragmented and dysfunctional family. And

I'm worried that Mom could relapse as soon as we get home. They talked about that on Family Night. The leader warned us that, as family, we can't blame ourselves if someone falls off the wagon. "It's their choice," he said somberly. "Just don't do anything to enable that choice and don't take the blame if they try to force it on you." He also warned us about button-pushing and establishing new ways of communicating as well as disconnecting. "It's time to establish boundaries," he explained. "And mutual respect." And, although I tried to listen, I felt over-whelmed. And now I'm worried I'll blow it.

We load Mom's stuff in the trunk and, although she of-fers to drive, I can tell she'd rather not. "I insist that I like driving now." And I partly do, but I'm not totally com-fortable behind the wheel. Still, I think I'm conscientious and careful. I don't speed or text and drive or anything even slightly dangerous.

Mom is pretty quiet for most of the drive. As we get close to town, she asks about tomorrow's celebration, and I confirm that it's still on.

"So everyone will be there?" she asks with a slight tremor to her voice.

Suddenly I'm worried. What if this stresses her out? "Just Grandma and Maddie that I know for sure. Dad never got back to me."

"That figures."

"It's not really a big deal," I assure her. "Just a way for

us to come together and acknowledge Hannah. You know, to honor her on her birthday."

"Well, I like that idea, Kiera. I think it's very thoughtful of you."

"Maddie was excited about it. And she is hoping she can stay home, Mom. She told me she's bringing all her stuff with her."

"And your grandma agreed?"

"I'm not sure it's her decision," I say cautiously. "You didn't give her guardianship of Maddie, did you?"

"No, of course not. But what did your dad have to say about Maddie coming home? Did he agree?"

"I don't know what he thinks. But I'm guessing he's talked to Grandma about it."

"I'm sure you're right."

As we drive past a grocery store, Mom asks if we need anything, but I assure her that it's all under control. I even go over the menu with her. "It'll be just a plain old barbecue. Like Hannah used to like on her birthday. Hamburgers and hotdogs. And I got potato salad and some things from the deli. So it's pretty simple."

When we get home, Mom excuses herself to her room to unpack and take a nap. Then feeling a little edgy—like I imagine a new parent might feel—I fuss around the house and do a load of laundry. I'm tempted to call my dad to see if he's coming tomorrow but decide not to push him. If he doesn't want to come, I'd rather he didn't. I doubt that Mom needs the stress of him being here against his will.

By two o'clock on Sunday, the time that I scheduled Hannah's party, Grandma, Maddie, Mom, and even Dad are all sitting outside. As they sit in the shade of our covered patio, I can see they're all on edge—especially Dad. He's wearing his sunglasses and a very grim expression. He clearly wishes he was someplace else. Probably the seventh green. They're all watching me, anxiously waiting for me to explain why we're here.

I pace around a bit, taking a moment to adjust the photo of Hannah's brightly shining face so that everyone can easily see it. It was taken around this time last year and enlarged for her memorial service. I force a nervous smile for my family, knowing it's time to begin—hoping I can do this.

"Thank you all for being here to honor Hannah today. As you know this would've been her eighteenth birthday. And, as you know, this is her diary." I hold up the pale blue faux leather book. "Which I hope you've all had the chance to read—the whole thing." I toss a curious glance at Dad. When he barely nods, I assume that means yes.

"Okay then." I glance around, grateful that my family members remain quiet…waiting. I can tell they're as uncomfortable as I am, but I'm determined to do this. "I want to read Hannah's last diary entry. Even though

we've all read it, I think we need to *listen* to it…together…
and as if Hannah were speaking to us." I nervously clear
my throat and begin to read.

December 31

> *I wanted to go to the New Year's Eve service at
> church tonight but eventually decided against it.
> I'm telling myself it's because I have to be up early
> for our youth group ski trip tomorrow. But in all
> honesty, it's because I didn't want to go to church
> by myself. I usually do go alone. And normally it
> doesn't bother me. But for some reason it did to-
> night.*

> *Naturally, Kiera wouldn't want to go. She nev-
> er does. And besides, she's at a sleepover, which is
> a good thing considering she's been sort of friend-
> less these past few months. And my parents
> planned to go out for the evening. Mom was
> dressed to the nines and ready for fun. So I encour-
> aged Maddie to go with me, but she said she was
> too tired. And since I didn't really didn't want to
> leave her home alone, I decided to stay in. Although
> that proved unnecessary since Mom and Dad
> wound up having a rather loud fight—and they
> stayed in too.*

> *So, here I sit in my sweet little room, having my
> own personal New Year's Eve service with God Al-
> mighty, Creator of the Universe, and Lover of my*

soul—which I must admit is pretty cool. First I listened to some inspiring music and read some uplifting Bible verses...then I spent time in prayer.

I'm so thankful and happy to be living the life that God has laid before me. I even peeked back to the beginning of this diary—one year ago—and I'm shocked at how much I've changed. It's like I'm a completely different person. And so very grateful for it. God is good! Truly good! And I know he has truly good things in store for me—throughout eternity!

The only thing that pulls me down right now is thinking about my family. I am so worried about each one of them. I've been praying and praying... but nothing ever seems to change. In fact, it seems to be getting worse. Hearing my parents' fight to-night was really disturbing. So much so that I checked on Maddie. To my relief she had on her earphones and her head was in a book.

So now I'm going to write out a special New Year's prayer for my family. Hopefully things will get better in the upcoming year.

Dear Father God,

I lift up my family to you—again. First of all, I lift up little Maddie. I pray that you will protect her from the anger that seems to be bubbling over in this house. I pray that you will show her how much you love her and that you have great things *in store for her. I pray that she will learn to put her trust in you. Please, use me in her life…let me be an example of your love.*

Next I pray for Kiera. I know she tries to act hard and cynical, but I can tell she's hurting underneath. I pray you'll break through that tough exterior and get right down to her tender heart. I pray you'll turn her around—let her see you and see how much you love her. Help her to fall solidly into your loving arms and be forever changed.

I pray for Mom. I know she's empty inside. I can see it on her face. She tries to fill that emptiness with everything—except for you. I pray you'll show her that her "fillers" are dead ends. I pray she'll look up and see that you are the only real answer—that you're the only one that can fill her up…and save her from herself.

I pray for Dad. He's empty too. He tricks himself into believing that all his activities and responsibilities are his life. Please show him it's a very empty life. Show him that he's neglecting his fatherly responsibilities. Show him that you're the only one who can teach him to be a good father. Because you are such a wonderful heavenly Father. Please, be a father to him. Bring him back to you. And back to us.

I pray for Grandma too. I know she serves you, Lord, but sometimes she can be too hard on the

ones who don't live the way she thinks they should.
Like Mom and Kiera. Please, help her to learn com-
passion. Show her that love is the answer. Lead her
in love so she can lead others in love.

Dear Father, I pray that you will shake up my
whole family in this upcoming year. I pray that
you will do whatever it takes to get their attention.
Shake them, break them, make them. I pray that by
the end of this year…each of them will have a whole
new relationship with you. And I pray this prayer
in real faith—I know you can do it, Lord. I believe
you will do it. I thank you for it!

Amen!

My voice is trembling by the time I say *amen* and now I can't hold back my tears. I'm both relieved and slightly scared to see that Mom, Grandma, and Maddie are crying too. I'm relieved that they seem to get this, but scared I pushed them too hard. I hope I didn't step over some invisible line.

"The reason I'm doing this today is for Hannah," I explain in a husky voice. "I want to honor her memory, and I want to honor her final prayer. The prayer she prayed on the night she died. I can't speak for anyone else, but I believe that God is answering her prayer—at least in regard to me. I'm not there yet, but maybe by the end of this year, I will be closer. At least I'm willing to try."

"I'm willing to try too," Maddie declares through her

tears. She comes over and wraps her arms around me. "I'll try to help you…if you'll help me."

I hug her tightly, promising to do my best.

Mom and Grandma quietly murmur that they want Hannah's prayers to be answered too…but I can tell they're still uneasy. Or maybe just worried. And Dad's not saying anything. Just sitting there like a stone. I'm about to ask him about it, when to my surprise, he stands. Hopefully, not to leave.

"I need to say something," he says in a gruff sounding voice. He removes his sunglasses to reveal that he's crying too. "I need to apologize to everyone. I need to admit that I'm the one to blame for Hannah's death. I realize I haven't taken full responsibility before, but if I hadn't allowed Hannah to get that car, she would still be alive." He clears his throat. "I'm sorry. And I'm sorry I didn't wake up that night and go get Kiera."

"It's not your fault, Dad." Maddie goes over to him, putting an arm around his waist. "Did you put the ice on the road that night?"

"Well, no, but—"

"Did you plant the tree that Hannah's car ran into?"

"Of course not."

"Are you God?"

Dad just frowns, then Maddie turns to me with a satisfied expression. "Tell him, Kiera. Tell him what you told me."

"You didn't control what happened that night," I firmly tell Dad. "No more than I did or Mom did or Grandma did or Maddie did. We might all feel guilty for various things, but none of us can take the blame for Hannah's death. We are not God. We are not in control of the universe."

"That's true," Dad agrees. "But I can still be sorry. And I need to tell all of you that I'm sorry for not doing a better job of being a dad. What Hannah wrote about me in her diary was true. I was failing all of you. I'm sorry."

"I was failing too," Mom says. "At everything."

"Well, it's not too late," Grandma declares. "We can all make changes. We can all do our best to make Hannah's prayer come true. With God's help we can."

December 31

The last four and a half months have been pretty interesting. Our family has continued to have its ups and downs. But it feels like the ups are winning. Maddie returned to her old school and even joined the swim team, which hasn't irritated her allergies—and her eczema is completely gone. Mom drops her off and either Dad or I pick her up.

Dad moved back home in late September, after he and mom went through some fairly intensive marriage counseling. They've had a couple of fights since he moved back, but nothing like it used to be. And they always apologize to each other and to Maddie and me afterward... even if it takes a while. Dad has also slowed down on golf—even before the weather turned cool.

Mom has continued with her recovery without a single relapse, which is considered unusual. But she religiously attends AA meetings and has made some good friends there. She returned to her real estate job about a month ago, but only works part time and never on weekends. And, although she still likes to shop sometimes, she's trying to keep it under control.

Although I decided not to emancipate myself, I did decide to graduate a year early from high school. I just feel ready for something more challenging. My parents support this decision, and I'm already taking college courses to finish off my requirements. Bernard has encouraged me to apply to his college. Yes, we have remained in contact, and I plan to visit his campus this spring. He took me to the Christmas Eve candlelight service at his beautiful church. It was amazing. And I was amazed in a completely different way when he kissed me good night.

But tonight, New Year's Eve, our whole family—including Grandma and Bernard—are attending the service at the same church where Hannah used to go...by herself. My good friends Marnie and Kent met us here, and we filled up the entire row, which I must admit feels pretty cool.

But the best part of all is that, while we're singing with

the rest of the congregation, I feel absolutely certain that Hannah is smiling down upon us. In fact, I feel fairly sure that she's singing and dancing—with joy.